"This book took six years to create.
Its pages are filled with dangerous adventures
and savage beasts,
but with great courage
you will carve a path to victory."

D.L.Lewis

My books have been bought by many people
in countries all around the world.
I am truly grateful to everyone who has encouraged
and supported my endeavours.
May the gamebook flame continue to burn brightly.

Battle Land Publishing
Based in England, U.K.

Book two in the Demon's Bane Series
Army of Bones

First Edition
Published 2021

Set in Times New Roman

ISBN: 978-1-9161250-3-2

Army of Bones

The Demon's Bane Series
Book Two

Written and illustrated by D. L. Lewis
Illustration for reference 195 by Helen Stimpson

Army
Of Bones

Introduction

Your homeland is smothered in dangerous forests and mist swept mountains. Its people live in fear of the foul Demons and dreaded beasts that stalk the moonlit nights. In order to survive, you have become an expert in the art of battle. You are a legend in your home world; a mighty adventurer who is revered across the land.

YOU are the Wizard's champion, slayer of the Demon Sorcerer and master of the blade. But your great deeds have attracted many powerful enemies.

A terrible shadow has risen from the Land of the Dead; an ancient evil with the power to destroy worlds. If you have any chance of defeating it, you will need more than just your brawn and wits. This time, you will need to make allies out of enemies.

You should begin by reading the **Rules of Play**.

Rules of Play

Life Force and Striking Speed

You will be asked to enter the following scores onto your Character Sheet. The sheet is located after the rules section.

Life Force - *Roll one six sided dice. Add 15 to the number rolled and enter the total into the Life Force box on your Character Sheet.*

Your **Life Force** reveals how healthy you are. You have been keeping yourself fit, so you will start your adventure in good shape. However, if you are hit or injured during the course of your adventure, your health may suffer. If your **Life Force** reaches 0 you are dead.

Important note: your **Life Force** may never exceed 30, as this is the maximum **Life Force** that a mortal may aspire to. Only Gods and certain other rare or magical beings may have higher scores than this.

Striking Speed - *Enter the number 10 in the Striking Speed box on your Character Sheet.*

You are swift with a blade - well versed in the art of battle - hence you start with a high score in this area. When engaged in close combat, whoever strikes fastest gains the advantage.

For reasons you will discover, many of your scores will change during the course of your adventure. It is important that you keep an accurate record of your scores.

Special Abilities

Pick two skills from the list below and enter them in the special abilities box on your Character Sheet.

Picklock - With this skill you will be able to pick almost any lock.

Scale - With this ability you will be able to scale anything, be it a wall or a cliff, no incline is too steep.

Haste - With Haste you will be able to run at incredible speed, if only for a limited time.

Stealth - With Stealth you will be able to walk with the softest of footfalls, allowing you to tiptoe in virtual silence.

Sixth Sense - Only a few ancient Wizards have found the time to fully master this skill. As you are a human warrior, your **Sixth Sense** will never be perfect. You will occasionally have premonitions of danger, forewarning you of imminent perils that your other senses cannot detect (for example, a concealed trap.) But remember, because you have not fully mastered the ability, it will not alert you to every hidden danger, so you will still have to be on your guard for much of the time.

Greater Wisdom - With Greater Wisdom you will have the ability to understand all languages. Whether it is the primitive speech of the Orcs, the obscure dialect of the Fairies or indeed any other language, you are a master of them all.

Close Combat

During the course of your adventure you will come into contact with many enemies.

When fighting opponents, you will need to look at your **Striking Speed**, **Life Force** and the chart with the headings **Focus**, **Move** and **Damage**. These can all be found on your Character Sheet.

In your homeland, invisible energy flows through the land and sky. It is in all places, moving slowly through the rocks, the trees and the rivers. No one knows what this power is, but many people call it the World's Spirit. Wizards trap small amounts of this energy in their staves and occasionally unleash it in the form of wondrous or violent spells. Other creatures - those who do not deal in magic - cannot sense the World's Spirit except at certain times. Only when in close combat can they feel the arcane power moving in the environment around them. Warriors and beasts then draw upon this energy to briefly increase their **Striking Speed**.

The rules for close combat are as follows:

1. Throw one dice to determine how much arcane energy you can draw from the world around you. Add your **Striking Speed** to the dice roll and make a note of the total. This is how fast you can attack this turn.

2. Now it is your enemy's turn to draw energy from the earth and air around it. Throw one dice and add your opponent's **Striking Speed** to the number rolled. This is how fast they can attack this turn.

If your total is higher than your enemy's, continue to number 3 of these instructions. If your enemy's total is higher, go to number 4. If both totals are the same, you and your opponent clash but neither inflicts harm on the other, so you must return to instruction number 1.

3. You strike before your opponent has time to act. Look on your Character Sheet and find the chart with the headings **Focus**, **Move** and **Damage**. Roll one dice to determine your level of **Focus**, then look at what **Move** you have performed. Reduce your adversary's **Life Force** by an amount that is equal to the **Damage** your **Move** has inflicted. Now return to number 1 of these instructions and continue fighting until either you or your opponent's **Life Force** reaches zero (death).

4. Your enemy strikes before you can act. Look at the chart underneath your opponent's **Life Force**, with the headings **Focus**, **Move** and **Damage**. Roll one dice to determine its level of **Focus**, then look at the **Move** it has performed. Reduce your **Life Force** by an amount that is equal to the **Damage** of your enemy's **Move**. Now return to number 1 of these instructions and continue fighting until either you or your opponent's **Life Force** reaches zero (death).

If your opponent dies, you may continue your adventure.
If you die, you must return to the beginning of the adventure and try again.

Fighting More Than One Opponent

Unless the text specifically states otherwise, you should treat multiple opponents as though they were a single enemy.

Magical Swords and Damage Bonuses

During the course of your adventure, you might acquire a rare sword which can increase the damage of your attacks. If you come across such a weapon and lose it at a later date, you must remember to remove the damage bonuses from your Character Sheet.

Ranged Weapons

If you find a ranged weapon such as a bow, the book will tell you when and how you can use it.

Equipment

If you have read The Demon Sorcerer, which is book one in this series, you may have gathered lots of loot and items during the course of your last adventure. To make room for new spoils, you leave these possessions at your home, safely locked in your booby trapped vault. You will set off on this adventure with a newly purchased **Long Sword**, a **Blanket**, a **Backpack**, and some **Crimson Coins**. (Your money will be discussed in more detail when the story begins.) You have also acquired a **Map** of the land to the north of the Druideen Mountains: it is opposite reference number 1, and you can view it at anytime once your adventure begins.

Final Words of Advice

Your quest will be perilous and it may take several attempts to reach your goal. Some of your enemies will try to destroy you with brute force, others may use deception, so you must always have your wits about you. If you are unsuccessful on your first attempt, do not despair. Failure is the opportunity to begin again more wisely, so make notes of any pitfalls that you want to avoid on future attempts.

Lastly, it is recommended that you make copies of the Character Sheets so that you can have them next to you whilst playing. If you do not want to do this, use pencil (not pen) in the Character Sheets in the book.

You are now ready to start your adventure.

You should begin by reading *The Story So Far…*

Character Sheet

Character's Name

Focus	Move	Damage
1	Sword Hilt Smash	1
2-3	Stabbing Thrust	2
4-5	Sweeping Blade	2
6	Heavy Sword Strike	3

Life Force
30 MAX

Striking
Speed

Special Abilities

☐ Pick Lock

☐ Scale

☐ Stealth

☐ Haste

☐ Greater Wisdom

☐ Sixth Sense

Character Sheet

Equipment

Crimson Coins

Notes

The story so far…

Five months ago, a cloak of terror had settled in every village and town south of the Enchanted Forest. The Demon Sorcerer was planning to gather an army and tear the land apart with the horns of war. Violence and carnage had looked certain, but chaos was averted thanks to a daring hero, who slew the Demon and fought a Dragon above the crumbling towers of a shadowy castle. You were that hero, and your victorious quest earned you a great deal of attention. Money and gifts were showered upon you, while songs were written about your bravery. Each week, travellers would arrive to ask about your adventures. You enjoyed the fame for a while, but at length you began to yearn for some peace and quiet. You counted your wealth and purchased a lonely castle on the edge of a lake, five miles north of the Druideen Mountains. The nearest village was a days' walk across rugged lands, so you felt certain to get a rest from the eyes of the world. However, just one week later, people began to arrive and ask about the time you fought with the mighty Demon. Not a day went by thereafter, without a knock at your door.

On a frosty morning, in the midst of autumn, you decided to go in search of a new adventure. You packed the plunder from your last quest into the vault beneath your home and set off in a northerly direction. You travelled light, taking with you only a pouch of coins, a recently purchased long sword, and a backpack that was waiting to be filled with new spoils. After several weeks, you finally reached the walled town of Mosal, in a region called Kostaria. The settlement was nestled on the edge of a mist laden pine forest, with rugged mountains rising up beyond the trees. The smoky taverns were full of interesting characters, many of whom were talking about the downfall of the Demon Sorcerer, but no one recognized your face. You sat back in peaceful obscurity, drinking ale and listening to the songs of the bards, the lyrics of which were mostly about you.

After an evening at the bar, you headed up to a rented bedroom, wrapped yourself under the bearskin covers and drifted off to sleep.

All through the moonlit night, the town was calm and quiet. You had no idea of the chaos that the morning would bring, nor of the great quest that was about to unfold.

Now turn to 1.

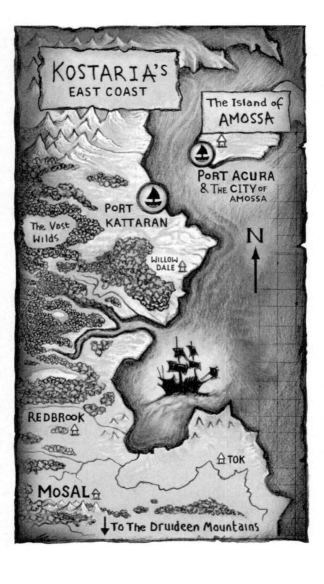

1
Illustration Opposite

You wake to the sound of a tolling bell, which echoes in the street beneath your bedroom window. A stony, grey dawn illuminates your room, and you rub your eyes with a weary expression.

Can it be morning already?

Several recollections from the night before filter into your mind; something about a keg of ale and a contest with a stocky drinker. Your money pouch is still tied to your belt, and you groan as you test its weight; it feels noticeably lighter compared to the morning before.

(Roll one dice and add six to the total. This is how many **Crimson Coins** are in your belongings. Make a note of it on your Character Sheet.)

Despite being snuggled under heavy bearskin sheets, you feel cold and shivery. The bell tolls again, this time more frantically, and you hear similar chimes ringing out all over the town. Wondering what is going on, you get to your feet and open the window. Frost clings to the glass, and a cold gust sweeps in. The autumn months are dying, and the early bite of winter is evident in the chill air.

"Arise! Arise!" calls a voice from below. You look down into the narrow street and see an elderly man clanging at a bell with his stick. People are coming out of their houses; some look flustered, while others look bewildered and half-asleep. He strikes the bell again, and his cry dispels the mugginess from your mind.

"Enemies at the gate!" he calls. "Enemies at the gate!"

You quickly dress and head down into the street, then the bell ringer hurries up to you and grabs you by the arm. "The town is under attack," he says. "Anyone with a weapon should head to the main gate. I see that you have a sword. You should make your way to the town's entrance as swiftly as possible!"

The people of this land are a hardy breed, but despite this, you can see an unmistakable glint of fear in his eyes.

"Who is attacking the town?" you ask. "Why would anyone attack Mosal?"

The man fixes you with a wide-eyed stare. "You wouldn't believe me if I told you," he answers. "Go to the gate and see for yourself." Then he is gone, off down the street, frantically striking his bell. Turn to **125**.

2

As you move further from the manhole, your surroundings become impenetrably dark and you have to feel your way along the slime covered wall. At length, the tunnel bends, then you see a light ahead. Pushing forward, you come to an area where glowing moss clings to the ceiling. You can now see a split in the tunnel, one way bearing slightly left and the other right. Bobbing in the water, wedged against the wall where the tunnels diverge, is a grisly looking skull. You have found the severed head of the villain who attacked you earlier.

Do you possess the special ability of **Sixth Sense**?

If you do, turn to **253**.

If you do not, turn to **335**.

3

You take a glancing hit to the brow, and the skin splits across your forehead. (Reduce your **Life Force** by two points.) You are almost knocked out by the blow, but Rowfur grabs your arm and steadies you, giving you a moment to shake yourself to your senses. Suddenly, your heart leaps in your chest with horror. A skeletal horse charges through the gate. The beast is clad in ancient armour and is being ridden by a grim Skeleton with flaming red eyes. It storms towards the line of men in a bid to smash its way through their ranks! Turn to **7**.

With Kazal dead, you kneel down next to Pelanthius. Your friend has started to regain consciousness, so you help him to his feet and tell him what happened. Whilst you are talking, the air suddenly grows colder. With an alarmed expression, you see the spirit of Kazal materialising in the air above his lifeless body. You reach for your sword, but something tells you to stop.

"Do not fear me," says the ghost. "By slaying me, you have freed me from the grip of madness." His voice is murky and ethereal, like a breathless whisper from another world. "Three weeks ago, one of my potions cursed me with a terrible side effect, and I was possessed by a violent insanity! There was no cure for me but death."

His image begins to fade, but Pelanthius calls out to him. "Kazal," he says, "a great danger looms over the world! We need your knowledge."

"Search the library beneath this tower," answers the fading voice. His transparent hand points towards a wall, then his image fades completely, and his ghostly form is gone forever.

After speaking some solemn words for his cousin's departed soul, Pelanthius heads over to the wall and finds a hidden door that leads to a dark, descending stairwell. The Wizard's glowing staff lights the way as you follow him down into a network of long, narrow corridors. At the end of one passage, you come to the secret library that Kazal spoke of. It is crammed with ancient books, several of which are filled with research on the mysterious Gods.

"Look here," you exclaim, "this should be of use to us." You pull a dusty tome from one of the shelves and flick through the pages. At the centre of the book is a section entitled, *Evoka: Legend of the War God*.

You suddenly feel incredibly weary, and you realise that your recent battle has taken a toll on your stamina.

"You should rest," says Pelanthius, who has noticed your exhaustion. "I will examine the book and tell you what I have learnt when you wake."

You thank him and lay down on a bench at the back of the room, where you drift into a deep sleep. (Increase your **Life Force** by one point.) When you rise, you find that Pelanthius has stopped reading. He is sitting on a high backed chair with a concerned expression. You ask him what is wrong.

"I have found a way to defeat Evoka," he says grimly. "But it will not be easy."

You listen as he tells his tale. Turn to **58**.

5

As you approach the bowing shelf, you notice the toad that you saw earlier. It watches you suspiciously as you scan the books. Each novel has been written in a strange language, and the ancient pages look tattered and worn.

If you have the special ability of **Greater Wisdom**, turn to **189**.

If you do not possess this special ability, you are unable to decipher the strange symbols, so you decide to explore elsewhere: return to **148** and pick an option that you have not yet chosen.

6

As the huge lump of iron tears through the Dragon's ribcage, its tail whips downwards and strikes the rampart with a forceful blow. Lumps of stone break loose and slam into you, nearly knocking you unconscious.

(Reduce your **Life Force** by three points.)

A moment later, the colossal beast falls apart. Its spine has been shattered by the giant arrow and its body breaks in two. You watch as the skull spirals loose and smashes through the roof of a building below, sending a cloud of dust up into the air. Turn to **175**.

7

Before you can act, Rowfur pushes you aside and leaps into the path of the charging steed. In an act of immense bravery, he manages to slay both the horse and the rider, but in doing so he is impaled by the shattered bones of his enemy. You leap to his side and catch him as he falls, but you find him dead in your arms. As the next wave of enemies pour in through the entrance, the defenders let loose their fury. In less than a minute, a mountain of smashed skeletal remains has piled up around the wreckage of the gate, and the enemy losses are enormous. However, in the savage chaos, a number of men also fall at the hands of the enemy. The defensive line is beginning to weaken, and several warriors look to you for advice. "My courage is willing," calls one, "but we cannot hold them back forever, the enemy numbers are simply too great."

Will you:

Tell the men to fight on, turn to **131**.

Or tell them to abandon the defence and head for the refuge of the town's central keep, turn to **365**.

8

The trail splits again, and this time the stallion surges to the left. You feel its muscles heaving with power, then the horse begins to pull away from the enemy. It slowly increases the gap, and the poisonous fog vanishes into the wooded depths behind you. The stallion speeds left and right along more branching trails, and you have soon escaped high into the range of wooded hills. A dire pain is now burning in your veins. You feel your consciousness slipping away, then darkness consumes your mind. Turn to **111**.

9

You instinctively roll to the left, and the point of the spear buries into the ground by your side, missing you by an inch. Your enemy draws back the weapon, but you leap to your feet and smash through its skull with your sword. Another enemy dives towards you, but Rowfur spins on his heel and obliterates it with a massive sword strike. You give your comrade a fleeting look of gratitude, then the fighting intensifies. More enemies pour in through the breach, swinging glowing swords above their heads. "Do not waver," bellows Rowfur, "we must hold them back at all costs!"

If you stay by Rowfur's side, turn to **140**.

If you think that the time has come to flee, turn to **351**.

Illustration Opposite

The great doors are pulled open and the guard leads you into a wide passage with gleaming white walls. You soon pass through another grand doorway, then another, before entering a huge hall in the heart of the building. It is a regal space indeed, with a high vaulted ceiling, but there are no guards within. You are curious to see that an immense stained-glass window has been covered with a tapestry at the back of the room, making the interior dark and shadowy. The throne looks empty in the gloom, but as you move forward you realise that Faranen is slumped upon it. He is clad in chest mail and animal skins, with a grey beard and shoulder length hair. His crown is tilted on his head, as if he is half-asleep.

"Who dares disturb me?" he mutters drowsily. "Did I not order that none should come before me?"

"My Lord," says the guard. "A traveller has come from afar, bearing knowledge of the undead hordes that gather on the mountain."

"Be away with the both of you," he says, slurring as if in a dream. "I am weary. Can you not see that I am weary?"

Ignoring his dismissal, you step forward and speak with a confident tone that demands attention. "I have knowledge that could save your people, Faranen," you explain. "If you listen to me, you may have a chance of halting this evil before it is too late. If you refuse to listen, your land will fall at the hands of the undead.

There is no time to waste here. Snap yourself from your stupor and heed my words."

The king slowly tilts his head to look at you... then you notice a strange sight. Hanging around his neck is a small glimmering object on a silver chain. You recognise it instantly as a Demon Stone, a cursed artefact which corrupts the thoughts of its wearer, making them paranoid and sick of mind.

"Where did you get that?" you ask, pointing towards the object.

"A gift," he says. "Now, I will not warn you again. Be away with you, for I must sleep and dream, to curtail this weariness that is upon me."

"You have been deceived, Faranen," you say sternly. "That object has brought a sickness upon your mind, and it has made you unfit to rule. It is draining your energy so that you cannot think clearly. That is why you sit and do not act, even though the hordes gather at your borders! A Demon, disguised as a friend, must have given it to you! Cast it away at once!"

"Do not give me orders!" snaps Faranen, suddenly finding the strength to raise his voice. He stands with an effort, waivers slightly, then steps down from his throne. His eyes are bloodshot and rimmed with darkness, but his energy seems to be returning. "I will not be insulted by a stranger in my own hall," he mutters, stepping closer. His feverish eyes turn towards the guard at your side. "You disobeyed my orders," he snarls. "I warned you not to disturb me, yet still you came into my hall!" Without warning, Faranen suddenly steps forward and strikes the guard with the pommel of his sword, knocking him unconscious. The king then spins on his heel and thrusts his blade towards you!

If you were forced to leave your weapons outside of the palace, turn to **191**.

If you are still carrying your weapons, turn to **63**.

11

The huge warhorse is heavily armoured, and its massive head is shielded by an iron plate. It is an imposing sight indeed, and it snorts fearlessly as you leap onto its back. At your command, it charges towards the gate, forcing the defenders to leap out of the way. The steed slams into the skeletal horde, and several wretched fiends are thrown down and trampled beneath its hooves. The grisly horrors try to grab the horse's armour, but the horde no longer has the numbers to stop you. You smash through their ranks, swerving around the necromancer, then you burst through the back of the enemy lines. An open track lays before you, so you gallop east before turning south towards a pine forest, leaving your opponents behind in the dust.

The Warlord instantly ends his assault on the town. The Skeletons collapse, then the dark figure rises into the air and flies after you. You realise that your plan is working, so you urge the horse into the forest.

As you hurtle along the pine wood track, you see your demented enemy sweeping through the dense shadows. He has transformed into a dark mist; a swirling, poisonous fog, with burning, coal-like eyes.

Huge murky hands with countless fingers reach towards you, and the horse's eyes flash with a look of terror. You try to stay ahead of your nemesis, to draw him further away from the town.

Suddenly, the woodland path splits in two directions.

If you take the sharp turn to the left, turn to **47**.

If you veer to the right, turn to **145**.

12

You ask her to tell you more about the three Demons who unleashed Evoka.

The Witch spits with repulsion. "Those wretched creatures do not realise the trouble they have caused," she growls. "Their lack of morality is wonderfully charming, but they have gone too far this time. They must be dealt with; they cannot be allowed to get away with this madness."

You agree that the Demons should be brought to justice.

"Very well," she mutters. "I will make a pact with you. My sisters and I will pay them a visit tomorrow. We will deal with the demonic trio, if you promise to set out on a quest to defeat Evoka."

You suspect that you are getting the harder end of the bargain, but you agree to the Witch's deal.

The crone drags her grisly, gnarled fingers through her hair, then she plucks a single strand from her head. She throws it into the fire beneath the bubbling pot, and there is a puff of purple smoke as it burns up in the flames. "The strand is burnt, and the deal is set," she says, as if enacting a strange ritual. "If you turn back now on your task, you will suffer the curse of the Witch."

"I will not go back on my word," you assure her.

She nods as if she believes you. "You have a hard task. Maybe even an impossible one. But I will give you some information that will help you in your quest."

Turn to **59.**

13

With swift reactions, you load your bow and release the arrow.

When you were in town, did you have a drink at the Wishing Well Tavern?

If you did, turn to **31.**

If not, turn to **137.**

14

Pelanthius agrees to wait with you. You seat yourself on the roots of a nearby tree, while the Wizard leans against a trunk. After half an hour, there is still no sign of the homeowner, and Pelanthius begins to puff tensely on his long pipe. "We are wasting time here," he mutters. "I cannot sit around and wait any longer, I am going to search for him in the town. Hopefully I will bump into him in one of the shops in Lore Street."

You have already wasted half an hour sitting here, so you decide to follow Pelanthius, in the hope that you will have better luck in town. Turn to **93**.

15

There is no sign of Pelanthius. He is not due to meet you for another half hour.

If you wish to sit and wait for him here, you may do so by turning to **97**.

Otherwise, you may use this time to explore a different part of RedBrook. If this is your choice, write the word **Time** on your Character Sheet, then choose a place that you have not yet visited.

If you now want to head for the Wishing Well Tavern, turn to **101**.

If you would rather explore Lore Street, turn to **27**.

If you want to take a walk along Beggar's Lane, turn to **54**.

If you want to investigate Sword Street, turn to **38**.

You summon all of your strength, and you hear a devastating crunch as your fist connects with Ugluk's jaw. Your opponent stumbles sideways and loses his footing, then he tumbles over the edge of the raised platform. Several onlookers leap out of the way as the massive brute crashes onto the floor, cracking the wooden boards beneath him. A stunned silence then sweeps over the room. People stare in disbelief. Some looked shocked, others horrified... then a massive cheer rises to your left. A group of people surge forward and lift you onto their shoulders, then you are carried from the stage. It would appear that a handful of gamblers bet on you to win, and their delight is obvious. A moment later you are put down near a desk where you collect your winnings. (Add **ten Crimson Coins** to your belongings.)

Ugluk is stunned by his defeat, and he clambers back onto the platform and demands a rematch. You decline his offer and head for the exit. Your supporters pat you on the back as you leave, chanting and showering you with praise. You tuck your winnings out of sight and decide to explore elsewhere. Turn to **198**.

The lightning sears towards you, but it is absorbed harmlessly into the strange glow that encases your body. Evoka pauses, momentarily perplexed… then his eyes suddenly flare like the stirred embers of a brooding fire. "So," he roars, not to you, but to the air around him, as if some unseen figure might be listening. "Tirasel! You treacherous shadow! You hide in your world of dreams, and instead of fighting your own battles, you aid a mortal in their quest to defeat me!" He laughs derisively, and his voice is so deep and mighty that it cracks the walls of the cave, sending segments of rock tumbling down from the ceiling. "Very well, let us see how your 'champion' fares against me. I will be impressed indeed, if your magic can protect this mortal against the might of my sword."

A massive, black sword suddenly appears by magic in his right hand, then he comes towards you, with gaping, snarling mouths.

Your enemy's whole body is shimmering with unimaginable power, and you know that you are about to fight the toughest battle of your life. Were it not for Tirasel's gifts, you would instantly be turned to dust by Evoka's attacks. But the blessings of the Goddess are about to give you a fighting chance.

Your godly armour will completely absorb the first eight hundred points of damage that Evoka deals to you, but after that, your protection will be gone.

Your second biggest ally is the **Dream-Sword**, which will magically double your **Speed** score for the duration of this fight. It can also cause massive, soul rending damage, capable of wounding even Evoka. The chart below shows the immense destruction that it can inflict: you should use this chart to determine your **Move/Damage** for the duration of this fight.

If your armour is destroyed, you must turn immediately to **377**.

Now let the battle commence:

YOU (whilst using Tirasel's Dream-Sword)
ARMOUR 800 STRIKING SPEED doubled

Focus	Move	Damage
1	**Dream-Sword Pommel Smash**	50
2-3	**Soul Rending Sword Strike**	50
4-5	**Wrath of the God-Sword**	100
6	**Cleaving Blade of Searing Light**	100

VS

EVOKA

LIFE FORCE 600 STRIKING SPEED 19

Focus	Move	Damage
1	**Claws of the Shadow King**	100
2-3	**Spell of Withering Agony**	100
4-5	**Hex of Shadows**	100
6	**Sweep of the Death-Sword**	200

If you win, turn to **138**.

The army stays put as the scout moves ahead on his own. However, before he can reach the bend, three of the ghostly spectres sweep from the sky and attack him. In a heartbeat, the lone scout is slain, and his body slumps to the ground like a withered husk. The ghoulish apparitions immediately race back into the grey clouds.

Arrows fly with futile vengeance from the Amossan archers, but the spirits are too high up to be hit. Their evil cackles echo down from the leaden sky.

"Leave them be!" says Faranen. "Do not waste your arrows." He decides that the army should stay together and push forward as one unit. Turn to **124**.

19

You close in on the robber and manage to trip his legs. He crashes to the ground, before leaping back to his feet. Realising that he cannot outrun you, he snatches another dagger from his belt. With a vile snarl, he lunges forward and thrusts the blade towards your heart!

This wretched villain has been plaguing the town of RedBrook for several months, and he is a merciless opponent.

RENARD THE THIEF

LIFE FORCE 6   STRIKING SPEED 8

Focus	Move	Damage
1	**Wild Punch**	1
2-3	**Devious kick**	1
4-5	**Elbow to the Throat**	2
6	**Stabbing Dagger**	2

If you win, turn to **385**.

As you get closer, you see that it is a group of men and women, one hundred strong. They are clad in armour, slowly making their way on horseback towards the sea beaten cliffs in the north. You cut diagonally up the slope to get ahead of them, then you stop and wait. They halt when they reach you, and their leader looks at you with grim eyes, his face flecked with ash.

"What happened to Port Kattaran?" you implore.

He wipes the ash from his bloodshot eyes. He looks tired and grim; a man who has seen too many horrors to ever know joy again. "You do not know?" he asks. "Have you been hiding under a rock?"

"There is no time to explain," you say. "Tell me what events occurred here."

He nods and begins talking. "The dark shadow, Evoka, returned several weeks ago. He destroyed the port, then he moved on, killing everything in sight. With every death, he grew more powerful, feeding on the souls of his victims. Always growing stronger. Always growing fiercer. The world is dying and the great forests have turned to ash in the burning rain. The mountains to the south have crumbled, and whole continents have fallen in a matter of days."

"A last alliance has gathered in the north," says a warrior maiden, who is seated at his side, "an army of men and Elves are preparing to make a final stand against Evoka, led by the Wizard, Pelanthius."

"Pelanthius!" you exclaim.

She nods. "We are heading to join his army. We may not win this battle, for Evoka's powers have grown beyond mortal reckoning. But we cannot sit and wait for death. You may ride with us if you wish, though I warn you, you should not hold much hope for victory."

If you agree to ride at her side, turn to **224.**

If you refuse, turn to **308**.

21

Your assailants collapse, but more enemies pour into view. Before you can catch your breath, you are set upon once more. As you parry a thrusting sword, your foot gets caught in the ribcage of a fallen enemy, causing you to tumble backwards onto the bone-strewn earth.

Before you can get up, a nightmarish figure thrusts downwards with a jagged spear.

If you have the special ability of **Sixth Sense**, turn to **9.**

Otherwise, turn to **41**.

22

Your challenge is accepted. The ominous figure waves his hand, then the Skeletons collapse into heaps of lifeless bones. The terrible figure stands alone on the battlefield, waiting for you. This will be a fight to the death. Turn to **74**.

23

You duck behind your shield, then the spears smash into it. You are jolted backwards and almost fall from the saddle! Your quick reaction probably saved your life, but your **Amossan Shield** has been cracked in two! Remove it from your inventory, then turn to **127**.

24

You carefully put the toad into your pocket. Its head pokes out over the top and it croaks merrily. It seems glad to be going with you, so you decide to give it a name. (Make up a name for your new pet, then write on your Character Sheet that the **Toad** is travelling with you.) Now turn to **195**.

Your brave rescue attempt inspires the other defenders, and several of them fight their way forward to help Rowfur. He is soon freed and the huge Skeleton is destroyed. Rowfur is now bleeding badly from several wounds, but he takes a weapon from a fallen rival and fights on like a furious barbarian.

If you hold your ground and continue fighting, turn to **75**.

If you decide to break free from the front line and run back into town, in the hope of recruiting more helpers, turn to **375**.

The time has come to leave, so you make your way back towards the tunnel's exit. As you are heading up the stairs, you see a small door which is slightly ajar. Pulling it open, you discover a storeroom that is stocked with water barrels and dried food. You are unsure how you missed it before, but it is a fortunate discovery.

You drink your fill and eat a hearty breakfast, (add three points to your **Life Force**,) then you leave the building.

Under the light of the pale stars, you both clamber onto Snowfire's back and take to the air.

Far below, the tiny lights of RedBrook glitter amidst a dark expanse of wilderness. It is still a few hours until sunrise, and a large moon peers at you between wisps of cloud. The lights of the town soon fade away, then you find yourself flying over the gloom of a shadow haunted forest.

It is now an hour before sunrise and the air feels bitterly cold. Pelanthius points towards the northern horizon. "Look there," he says. "Can you see that distant patch of darkness, hovering in the moonlit sky?"

You nod and ask him what it is.

"My magic tells me that it is a gathering of birds. They are Evoka's spies and they are scouting this area. We should hide swiftly, before they get close enough to see us."

You trust the old Wizard's intuition, so you quickly form a plan.

If you tell Pelanthius to set down in a clearing amidst the trees, so that you can hide in the forest, turn to **285**.

If you advise him to veer slightly to the east, where the sky is weighed down with clouds, turn to **105**.

27

Lore Street is a narrow, cobbled lane that is cloaked in the shadows of tall, crooked buildings. A few mysterious people hurry past you, draped in hooded cloaks with their heads ducked. Peculiar looking shops are dotted along the street, bearing odd and mystical names. Looking in through their windows, you see a clutter of complex apparatus that looks more suited to the interests of a spellcaster than a warrior. You wonder if Pelanthius's cousin might be here, but as yet, you can see nobody that fits the description of an ancient Wizard. The winding street seems to go on forever, but eventually you come to a dead end. Facing you is an old, decrepit shop, the last one in the street. You see a faded sign above the door which reads: *Rajenji's Rare Potions*. You decide to take a look inside.

Turn to **159**.

28

When you are halfway across, you notice a crack opening up in the stone beneath your feet. You realise that the whole bridge is about to collapse, so you leap over the glowing lake towards the other walkway.

As you spring across the gap, your leg is struck by a spitting blob of lava.

If you are wearing the **Ethereal Armour of the Immortals**, turn to **398**.

If not, turn to **352**.

Illustration Opposite

You follow Clayton as he charges along the walkway. "We haven't seen Dragons in these parts for years," he says, "but once upon a time they were common in these skies. There's an old weapon on the high tower, designed to fend off such beasts in case of an attack, but it hasn't been used for generations. I can't say if it will still function, and I don't even know if it will work against this undead horror, but it's the only idea that I can think of." You decide it is worth a try, so you both race up onto the roof of a nearby tower. A huge, strange contraption stands before you, crafted from wood and steel, with massive cogs and wheels. It looks something like a crossbow, but it is twenty feet across, with a seat at the centre. "I'll work the pulleys at the back of the machine," says Clayton. "If they still work, I should be able to aim this thing. You get into the control seat. When I give the call, pull the lever to fire." As you clamber into the seat, Clayton rushes off behind you, then you hear a clunking and whirling coming from the contraption. You can see the skeletal Dragon soaring towards the town, growing closer by the second. As the huge war-machine turns into position, the monstrous beast changes direction and soars towards you.

"Now!" screams Clayton, "fire the weapon!" You look down and to your horror you see not one, but two rusty levers at the side of your chair.

If you pull the black lever, turn to **71**.

If you pull the red lever, turn to **89**.

You step forward and inform the guard that you have only just reached the city, having sailed here from Port Kattaran. "Your people are in more danger than you realise," you tell him. "I have important knowledge of the troubles that have beset this region. You must let me speak to King Faranen. The fate of this land depends on it."

The guard narrows his eyes and you see that you have gained his interest. "What is it that you know?" he asks. "What knowledge do you have, that warrants disturbing the great Lord Faranen?"

If you wish to reveal the nature of your quest, turn to **122**.

If you tell him that you will only explain your story to the King, turn to **136**.

31

The brew is still swirling through your veins and it is marginally affecting your aim. The arrow narrowly misses Kazal's head and crashes into the wall, spinning away from him in a shower of sparks.

(Remove **one Arrow** from your belongings.)

You quickly reach for a second arrow, but you are too late!

Turn to **141**.

32

The box is filled with hay-like material, on top of which rests three glass jars. In the first container you see a large eyeball floating in yellow fluid. In the second you see an assortment of teeth. With a grim look, you pick up the third jar. The glass is tinted black and there is no telling what lies inside. You carefully uncork it and tip out the contents. You half expect something horrendous to appear, so you are surprised and relieved when six coins drop out into the palm of your hand. You have a feeling that the Witch stole the money from someone else, so you do not feel bad about taking it.

(Add the **Crimson Coins** to your possessions.)

There is nothing else of interest in the chest, so you decide to search elsewhere.

Return to page **148** and pick an option that you have not yet chosen.

33

You climb onto the back of the horse and seat yourself behind Pelanthius. The majestic steed spreads its wings, and a moment later you soar up towards the clouds.

"The task ahead of you is immense," says Pelanthius. "We must visit my cousin, Moras Kazal, for he has always been fascinated by stories of the Gods. He spent many years researching the subject, so if anyone would know how to defeat Evoka, it would be him."

"How long will it take to reach him?"

"On foot it would take a week, but Snowfire will get us there in less than a day. Kazal lives in a clearing in the Whispering Woods, near to the town of RedBrook. I have not seen him for over three years, so I am sure that he will give us a warm welcome." You agree to the Wizard's plan and you swoop off towards your new destination. For the next few hours, vast plains and roaring rivers pass beneath you. Valleys and hills come and go, like distant folds on the landscape, and the blustery air reddens your cheeks. Sometime in the afternoon, you set down in a forest clearing and dismount from your steed. At the centre of the glade, a circular tower rises up above the roof of the forest. Its walls are covered in ivy and all looks still and quiet. Pelanthius knocks on the door, but there is no answer. He grumbles under his breath, peering at the upper windows in the hope of seeing movement. "It would seem that my cousin is out," he says at length. He shakes his head in frustration, then he pauses to think. "Kazal has a great passion for making potions," he says. "He has probably gone to visit the nearby town of RedBrook, to buy some ingredients. I advise we go and look for him straight away. The town is only a short walk through the woods."

If you wish to explore RedBrook, in the hope of finding him there, turn to **93**.

If you try to break into the building, turn to **221.**

If you tell Pelanthius that you would rather sit by the tower and wait for Kazal to return, turn to **14**.

34

People place bets as you climb onto the platform. Ugluk looks even larger up close, and his eyes are confident and fierce. Your challenger repeats the rules, which are very simple. "No weapons, no kicking, no biting, just punching. First person to be knocked down loses." He grins at you, and his eyes narrow. "Good luck, brave one. You're going to need it."

The crowd suddenly cheer as your opponent surges forward, swinging his fist towards your head. His sudden lunge catches you off-guard and you take a massive impact to the skull.

(Reduce your **Life Force** by two points!) If you are still alive, you stagger sideways, barely managing to keep your footing. You shake yourself to your senses as Ugluk rushes towards you once more. His fist is drawn back, poised to unleash a second strike.

If you swing your fist at Ugluk's head, turn to **222**.

If you adopt a defensive stance, turn to **216**.

35

You expect that Pelanthius is unaware of the recent troubles at Kazal's tower, so you hurry into the wood in the hope of catching up with him. Twisting branches join overhead, and the trail looks far more sinister now that the sun has vanished. A few thin slivers of moonlight penetrate the arching roof. Then the leaves start to rustle, as if a cold wind is blowing over the treetops.

Up ahead, you spot a narrow stream crossing the path. You vaguely recall seeing it earlier in the day, but now that night has fallen you notice something different about it. The gurgling water is awash with a toxic fluorescence and the nearby trees are shimmering with a strange, green aura. Turn to **79**.

36

In a desperate act, you pull out the wand which you took from the Witch's hut. You have no idea how to use it, but your enemies do not know that, and you hope that the mere sight of it will send them into a panic. You quickly yell some meaningless words at the top of your lungs, pretending to know what you are doing, then you start to wave the crackling wand through the air. A sudden look of horror appears on your enemies' demented faces. Even the undead seem to know the power of a Witch's wand, and a shriek of dread escapes from their misshapen mouths. They soar upwards, fleeing back into the sky, then they vanish from your sight into the gloom ridden clouds.

Turn to **107**.

37

You move with lightning reflexes, narrowly avoiding the blast.

"A swift little enemy," Kazal hisses. "But I have ways of dealing with your kind!" He spins on his heel and points his staff towards an old, dusty suit of armour. With strange, clanking movements, it comes to life and stalks towards the unconscious body of Pelanthius.

With a look of horror, you rush across the room to protect your defenceless friend. You swipe at the armour, causing the metal shell to dent under the impact, but your enemy does not fall. It judders briefly, then turns towards you, swinging its axe with murderous intent.

You have no choice but to fight this bizarre automaton. As the battle continues, Kazal watches intently from the far side of the room.

MAGICALLY ANIMATED ARMOUR

LIFE FORCE 9   STRIKING SPEED 8

Focus	Move	Damage
1	Hilt Slam	1
2-3	Wild Strike	2
4-5	Sweeping Blade	3
6	Downward Axe Chop	3

If you win, turn to **245**.

38

You soon find yourself at the entrance to a winding, cobbled street. Market stalls are everywhere, and people are bustling to and fro in the hope of finding a bargain. The street soon begins to bend to the left and you notice a hunchbacked fellow standing by a makeshift table. It is covered in all sorts of clutter, but the items look tarnished and overpriced. As you walk past, he calls out to you in a croaky voice.

"Got anything to sell?" he says, "I'm always looking for new merchandise."

If you are wearing **Ariana's Necklace**, the trader will give you **six Crimson Coins** for it.

If you have a **Black Crystal Necklace**, you may sell that to him for **five Crimson Coins**.

If you have neither of these items, there is nothing that he wants from you at this time.

Make any necessary adjustments to your Character Sheet, then, when you are ready to move on, turn to **185**.

39

You stoop over the table and peer at the scattered objects. They are small clippings of worthless metal, fused together to form odd, humanoid shapes. You are unsure of their purpose. At any rate, they are of no value to you. Pushing them aside, you cast your eyes over a bundle of cloth that sits beneath the fading flame, and you find **three Crimson Coins** tucked inside. (Add them to your belongings.)

If you want to keep searching, you must pick an option that you have not yet chosen.

If you investigate the mysterious chalk markings, turn to **297**.

If you look inside the bowls, turn to **227**.

If you are ready to leave, turn to **129**.

40

The chaos that has beset the town is only worsening. You know that the sewers lead beneath the outer wall. If you take that route, you might be able to escape without getting caught in the fighting.

If you want to look for a way into the sewers, turn to **70**.

Otherwise, you will have to stay with the archers, turn to **65**.

Or offer your help at the main gate, turn to **130**.

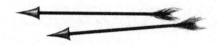

41

You roll to the right and narrowly avoid being impaled by the spear. Nonetheless, the jagged edged weapon still glances your head, gashing the side of your face. (Reduce your **Life Force** by two points.) As your enemy draws back the spear for a second attack, Rowfur suddenly sees that you are in trouble. He spins on his heel and obliterates your opponent with a massive sword strike, splitting its skull in two. You leap up, but you have no time to thank your comrade. A new wave of enemies pour in through the breach, wielding jewel encrusted swords.

If you wish to continue fighting, turn to **140**.

If you decide that the time has come to flee, turn to **351**.

The Witch's bed is hard and lumpy, but nonetheless, you quickly fall into a deep sleep. When the first light of dawn sweeps over the hut, you hear a loud voice outside and the front door suddenly bursts open with a crash. You leap out of bed and see a tall, old man standing in the dawn-lit entrance. Upon his head is a large, pointed hat with a wide rim, and he is graced with the longest silver beard that you have ever seen. He is dressed in a flowing patchwork of colourful robes, and in his gnarled old hand is a crooked staff which is shimmering with power. You recognise the man at once: he is Pelanthius, the head of the Wizard's Council.

You hear him calling out your name, so you step into the living room.

"Thank goodness you are alive," says Pelanthius, when he catches sight of you. "I heard that you were trapped here and that you were going to be eaten by a Witch!" He spins around, looking for your captor, and angry sparks of red light leap from the tip of his staff.

You calm the Wizard down and explain the truth. As you retell the events of the last few days, you see his bushy eyebrows rising with surprise. Then, when you have finished, he sits down on a chair. For a minute he muses in silence, then he turns towards you with a most serious look. "I would like to call the Witch a liar," he says, "but it sounds as if she is telling the truth. My sleep has been troubled of late, and I feared that a terrible event would soon come to pass. Two days ago, I dreamt that a mighty shadow was rising up through the ground.

It spread across the land like a mist of death, bringing terror in its wake. I realise now that this was no mere nightmare, but a vision of the future."

"The Witch said that you might know a way to defeat Evoka."

Pelanthius shakes his head. "Evoka is a mighty entity indeed. I do not know how to defeat him. However, I do know a man who might be able to help us. His name is Moras Kazal."

"Who is Moras Kazal?" you ask.

Pelanthius rises to his feet. "I will tell you on route," he says. "We have much to do, and no time to squander."

You follow Pelanthius as he hurries towards the door.

Before he exits the hut, he suddenly pauses and looks back.

If your **Life Force** is thirteen or less, turn to **88**.

If your **Life Force** is fourteen or more, turn to **243**.

43

Nothing should now stand between you and the portal, yet something tells you that a final test may lurk ahead. You decide that it would be wise to keep Pelanthius at your side. Gripping your sword, you lead the small group up the shadowy gorge. By midday, the world starts to grow darker and you push into a swathe of grim and brooding cloud. You slow your ascent, picking your way between sharp claws of rock, whilst distant thunder rattles in the west. A storm has gathered somewhere out to sea, but it does not make land and you are spared the freezing deluge of late autumn rain.

An hour before sundown, you come upon a narrow set of steps that have been chiselled into the rock.

"The steps of Mantium," says a half-breathless soldier. "They were cut into the rocks long ago, by the old kings of Amossa. We are not far from the top now, not far from that ghastly portal."

The soldier is right. You see that the steps are ascending towards a large cave. Your senses tell you that the gateway lies within it. Turn to **158**.

44

Suddenly, Pelanthius bursts up through a hatchway behind you. He has arrived late to the battle, but his presence is welcome indeed. As he lifts his staff, you suddenly notice five massive battleships racing out of the storm. The fleet has appeared as if from nowhere, and they are flying the flag of Lord Mortan, who is a well-known Pirate slayer. In an instant, the alarmed villains spin on their heels and scramble towards the safety of their vessel. They are soon fleeing in horror, vanishing into the veil of the storm. With your enemies gone, Lord Mortan's fleet fades like a mist on the wind, and you realise that the ships were a mere illusion, created by the Wizard.

Fornax staggers towards you. "I have come to the conclusion that I would always like a Wizard and a warrior on board," he exclaims with a look of gratitude. "I saw you bring down the legendary Blood-Gor. And that magic trick was also a sight to behold! I will be telling *this* tale for a few years to come!"

Suddenly, a flustered crewman appears through a hatchway and runs up to Fornax. He claims that the ship is taking on water, due to its collision with the enemy vessel. With a worried look, Fornax heads below deck to assess the extent of the damage.

Turn to **51**.

The guards usher everyone along the stony shoreline. When you reach a secluded part of the bay, they lead you towards a large boulder that is resting against the cliffs. With a heave, they push the rock aside, revealing a secret tunnel. You follow them into the gloom, and the passage soon begins to slope upwards. Ten minutes later, you pass through a large iron door which opens into a moonlit courtyard. The area is scattered with heavily armoured guards, and you realise that the tunnel has taken you onto the flat lands above the cliffs, into the walled city of Amossa.

To the north, looming above the rooftops of the metropolis, you can see a distant and lonely mountain, jutting up like a black claw of rock.

"That is the peak of Illomen!" says Pelanthius. "There is our destination."

One of the guards follows your gaze, then turns to speak with you. "We call it The Claw, here in Amossa. But The Mountain of Death would probably be a better name for it now. It is crawling with the undead, or at least it has been ever since the black gate appeared near its peak."

"The black gate?" you ask.

He nods grimly. "It appeared without warning, spewing ghastly magic across the land. The dead have risen from their graves, and they have gathered all over the slopes."

"We must find a way to close that gate," you say, "or things will soon go from bad to worse. The walls of this city might protect you for the moment, but that will not be the case for long."

The man's eyes narrow, as if agreeing with your words. "You may be right," he concedes, "but to destroy the gate, we would have to reach it first. And therein lies the problem. An army of barbarians would struggle to fight their way through the hordes that surround it. If a person were to have any chance of reaching that portal, they would need the backing of King Faranen's army, but he does not seem eager for war."

If you would like to speak with King Faranen, you should head for his palace in the heart of the city. If you want to take this course of action, turn to **157**.

If you would rather continue your conversation with the soldier, to see what more you can learn, turn to **85**.

After a few moments, he blinks, then looks surprised, as if seeing you for the first time. "Who are you?" he snaps. "What are you doing here on my hill? My pet will see to you! Get rid of this intruder! Attack! Attack!" he shouts.

You are suddenly knocked onto your back, as if by a blast of wind. Before your very eyes, a Spirit Wolf begins to appear out of the air, glowing with a ghostly aura! The beast stalks towards you, but a flash of light erupts from Pelanthius's staff, momentarily dazzling it. The Wizard pulls you to your feet, then you both hurry over the top of the hill.

Turn to **336**.

As you turn left along the narrow trail, you see a fallen tree which is blocking the path ahead. In a desperate, split second manoeuvre, the horse tries to leap the obstruction.

Roll one dice to see if luck is on your side.

If you roll a one or a two, turn to **72**.

If you roll any other number, turn to **94**.

You crush the skull of your fallen enemy with the pommel of your sword, prompting a sudden cheer from the archers. But their victorious cry does not last long, as the abominations are now climbing over the top in heavy numbers. In a matter of seconds, a bloody fight erupts along the walkway as groups of brave archers try to hurl their attackers back over the battlements. With no swords to hand, they are fighting a tough battle, so you do your best to help them. Murderous forms leap towards you from both sides, hacking and slashing with their rusty weapons.

(As soon as you have reduced the Horde's **Life Force** to twenty or below, turn to **98**.)

THE HORDE

LIFE FORCE 30   STRIKING SPEED 8

Focus	Move	Damage
1	Pommel Slam	1
2-3	Lunging Spear	2
4-5	Sweeping Axe	3
6	Mighty Sword Strike	3

Illustration Opposite

Your opponent is an apex predator who has been roaming this forest for a long age. It has never retreated from a battle, and it will fight you to the death!

MOON GIANT

LIFE FORCE 20		STRIKING SPEED 8

Focus	Move	Damage
1	Life Stealing Aura	2
2-3	Freezing Breath	3
4-5	Giant's Punch	5
6	Death Stare	See Below*

(*Special Move: If the Giant attacks you with its Death Stare, beams of deadly light will erupt from its four eyes. In desperation, you duck and weave in an attempt to avoid the rays. Roll one dice and add two to the total; this is the amount of damage that is inflicted on you.)

If you win, turn to **78**.

"This gate will not hold for much longer," shouts Rowfur. "If we have any hope of survival, we cannot let the enemy get a footing inside these walls. Only the Gods can say what brought this curse upon us, but we are a hardy people, and we have never bowed to any foe. Gather your courage, and let us send these enemies back to the pits from whence they came."

A huge, gaping crack suddenly appears at the centre of the gate. Rowfur hunches his shoulders with a fierce expression, gripping his sword with both hands. "Ready yourselves!" he roars.

The entrance is suddenly ripped apart and a host of nightmarish figures swarm in through the gap.

One man panics and spins on his heel. "Why are these things attacking us?" he yells. "We have to escape! We cannot fight an army of the dead!" He pushes his way back through the defenders and runs away into the town. Two men from the back of the group follow him, but the rest stand firm.

If you follow the deserters, turn to **190**.

If you hold your ground, turn to **91**.

After surveying the ship, you discover that The Sea Star has been damaged, but is still seaworthy.

"We should make it safely to Acura," says the captain, "but she'll not make the journey back, not in this state. We'll have to dock at Acura for a few weeks to get her repaired."

Secretly, you are unconcerned by this news, as you are still on track to reach your destination. After a few hours, the storm has passed and a blustery dawn paints the sky in purple shades. A good wind fills the sails and no more perils disrupt your passage. Come early evening, you head downstairs for a hearty meal, which you enjoy alongside the other sailors.

(Increase your **Life Force** by two points.)

When you are done, you return to the upper decks. As night draws in, you hear the lookout's voice ringing out from the perch on the mast. "Land ahoy," he bellows. "Land ahoy!"

Pelanthius appears through the hatchway, and you both walk to the bow of the ship and peer into the darkness. The lights of Acura begin to glitter in the distance, and you see that the port is nestled in a bay at the foot of the sea cliffs. You slowly sail towards it.

Turn to **118**.

The Witch shakes her head. "Two centuries after Evoka was banished, the Gods had a great war that raged for many years. Several of the most powerful deities were obliterated during that great cataclysm, and their remnants became many of the stars and galaxies that you see today. Locked in his underworld kingdom, Evoka was safe from the war. He is now one of just a few deities left in the cosmos, and it is unlikely that the others will be in a rush to confront him. Take the Dream Goddess, for example. She is the most peaceful of the Gods. Even if she wanted to help us, I am not sure that she could. She exists only in the Land of Dreams and she is neither cunning nor terrible like Evoka." The crone shakes her head despondently. "We cannot rely on the help of others. This is our mess and we must tackle it ourselves."

Turn to **12**.

Pelanthius soon rejoins you, then you continue down the narrow lane. You are both interested in different shops, so you decide to part ways. "Meet me back here when you have finished exploring," says the Wizard. "Don't be long though! We still have a quest to complete." He then ducks into a nearby building, which sells items that are catered for spellcasters.

You walk down the lane to see what else it has to offer, and you soon come to a split in the trail.

In the left-hand turning, you can see several shops lit by green candles. In the right-hand lane, you can see shops with red candles.

If you turn left, turn to **346**.

If you turn right, turn to **307**.

54

Beggar's Lane leads into a labyrinthine network of narrow alleyways, where tall, shabby buildings drape you in shadow. It is clear that you have come into a run-down area. There is barely enough room for people to squeeze past each other, and an unpleasant smell fills the air. As you turn a corner, you hear footsteps behind you. A slim man barges past and runs away down the alley. It takes you a split second to realise that your money pouch has been snatched from your belt, so you quickly give chase. Suddenly, the Thief turns and hurls a rusty dagger towards you.

Roll one dice to see if luck is on your side.

If you roll a five or a six, you are lucky: the Thief's aim is inaccurate and the blade sweeps past you, thudding into the wall of a wooden building.

If you roll a four or lower, the blade slices your leg: reduce your **Life Force** by two points.

If you are still alive, turn to **248**.

Suddenly, several Skeletons collapse nearby, without being hit. You scan the area and see the same thing happening all across the battlefield. It is as if the wretched nightmares have started to lose the source of their power!

Through the thinning horde, you catch sight of the tall, shadowy figure who you saw from the rampart. Dark energy still crackles around him, but he now looks drained and exhausted.

"There is the Necromancer!" says a man to your right. "He is the cause of this chaos!"

"His power is diminishing," says a second man. "Swiftly! Let us cut our way to his side and slay him while we have the chance."

If you want to lead the men into the heart of the battle, in an attempt to cut your way towards the leader of the foul army, turn to **200**.

If you dash through the thinning ranks and try to reach the warlord on your own, turn to **74**.

If you stay where you are, and tell the defenders to hold their ground, turn to **150**.

56

The chest has been sealed with a large, black padlock.

If you have the special ability of **Picklock** and wish to use it, turn to **32**.

If not, you must return to page **148** and pick an option that you have not yet chosen.

Leaping a mass of tangled roots, you burst into the clearing at the top of the hill. Kazal's tower looms darkly, rising up against the moonlit night. You see that a yellow candle has been lit behind one of the upstairs windows, so you know that somebody is now at home. Looking around, you see Snowfire waiting loyally nearby, but he looks agitated and he is scuffing and stomping the ground, as if trying to tell you something. The narrow door to Kazal's tower is slightly ajar and, as you edge towards it, you see the body of Pelanthius lying on the floor within! Throwing caution to the wind, you sweep inside and kneel beside him. He has been knocked unconscious by a heavy blow to the back of the head, but he is still alive. Despite your efforts, you are unable to wake him.

Within the tower, candles burn on the walls, sending dancing shadows across the stone flagged floor, and suits of ancient armour stand on display. Stairs rise to a balcony on your right, and all is ominously quiet.

Somewhere nearby, you hear the creak of an opening door, then a sinister voice echoes from a gloomy corner of the room. "So," it mutters. "Another thief has come to steal my secrets." There is an edge of insanity to the voice, and you spin around to see Kazal standing in the shadows like a leering spectre. He is dressed in a tattered patchwork of robes and his grey hair and long beard hang down in an untidy mess. His eyes are wide and bloodshot, like a man consumed by madness.

"Now I see proof of my fears," he snarls. "First my cousin comes to steal the secrets of my potions, and now he has sent an assassin to kill me!" His eyes darken. "Pelanthius was a powerful Wizard, so it was good fortune that I foresaw his treachery. He would have proved a mighty adversary had I not tricked him and launched a surprise attack."

"Your cousin did not come to harm you, Kazal," you tell him. "He came only to ask for your help. A terrible evil threatens this land and we cannot defeat it without your aid. Your mind has been twisted by paranoia."

"Lies!" he snaps. "You have come to deceive me, to steal my magical potions! But I am wise to your deceitful ways!" His eyes grow wider and his staff suddenly glows with an immense, surging power. "I am no fool," he mutters. "I know an assassin when I see one!"

A beam of white light suddenly leaps from his staff and flashes towards you.

If you dive to the left, turn to **37**.

If you dive to the right, turn to **102**.

"Evoka cannot be destroyed by mortal weapons," explains Pelanthius. "He is simply too powerful. But all hope is not lost. If we can reach the gateway between our world and his, and destroy it whilst he is resting in the River of Souls, he will be trapped in the Underworld once more. But we will have to be fast. The Witch informed you that Evoka will return in six moons, so that leaves us five days to complete our quest. If we fail to destroy the gateway in that time, Evoka will return to wreak havoc once more, and we will not survive another encounter with him."

You take out your map and flatten it on a nearby table. "The Witch said that the gate resides near the peak of Illomen, somewhere on the island of Amossa," you say.

Pelanthius nods. "On foot it would take us a long while to reach it, but with Snowfire's help we might get there just in time." He holds up a small, glittering object. "It is a good thing that we came here," he says, "for I found this artefact tucked behind some papers at the back of a shelf."

"What is it?" you ask, peering at the strange oval object.

"It is a magical compass. Vast storms gather every winter over the forests to the north of RedBrook. If we encounter one, we may well become disorientated. Kazal's compass never fails to point north, so we should never lose our way."

You rise from your seat. You now have everything you need to progress with your adventure.

If you wish to set off immediately for Amossa, turn to **26**.

If you wish to explore your surroundings first, by wandering through the network of tunnels, turn to **205**.

59

"Evoka is a mighty enemy," she croaks, "but his time in the Underworld has slowed him down and weakened him. He has grown haggard and gaunt, like a once mighty wolf, who for too long has been locked in a cage."

"He did not seem weak and feeble yesterday!" you exclaim.

The Witch nods. "His powers are incredible, but he is capable of much more. If he is given time to stretch his wings, so to speak, he will become far more dangerous. Hence you must act swiftly, before his full might returns."

"Where is he now?" you ask.

"His recent tirade has tired him, and he has been forced to return to the Land of the Dead, to rest in the River of Souls. If my calculations are correct, he will re-emerge in six moons time. You have until then to come up with a plan. If you have not done so by that time, it will probably mean the end for you. And the end of us all."

"Then you had best tell me how to defeat him, for he seemed almost invulnerable yesterday. What weaknesses does he have?"

She shakes her head. "I do not know," she admits. "But the Wizards of Lore may have the answer to that. I will send them a letter, telling them to meet you at my hut."

"The Wizards of Lore will not trust a letter from a Witch," you tell her.

She nods thoughtfully. "You are quite right," she says. "I have played tricks on them in the past, so they are unlikely to accept my invite." She rubs thoughtfully at her prickly chin, then she clicks her fingers. "I will write a letter informing them that I have captured you, and I will say that I intend to eat you at first light. The Wizards are a bunch of hideous do-gooders, so they will surely come here in the hope of rescuing you. Yes indeed! That should get them moving," she says, cackling with delight. She steps down from the chair and shuffles over to the front door. "You can stay in my hut until first light," she says, "by which time I suspect that your friends will arrive. As for me, my sisters and I will deal with Ganthor, Korovar, and Golgorast." She takes a broomstick from beside the door and steps outside. "Good luck in your quest, foul human. If you manage to succeed in this task, the world will surely owe you a great debt." With that, she slams the door and flies off into the night.

When you check the door, you find that it has been sealed by a powerful spell. There is no way to open it.

Turn to **148**.

A headless, skeletal figure stalks out of the gloom. It is glowing with an aura of magic and its fingers look like sharpened daggers of glittering bone. By the rotting clothes that hang from its body, you can tell that the abomination was once a resident of Mosal; a murderer who was put to death by the locals. His body was probably dumped into the sewers, but he has been revived by the dark magic that is affecting the town, and he seems eager for vengeance.

The headless figure shuffles forward, forcing you to defend yourself.

HEADLESS HORROR

LIFE FORCE 9   STRIKING SPEED 8

Focus	Move	Damage
1	Raking Claws	1
2-3	Strangling Grasp	1
4-5	Jagged Bone Fingers	2
6	Frenzied Attack	4

If you win, the bones tumble into the water and sink beneath the surface. Turn to **2**.

61

A sudden blast of energy strikes the phantoms, causing them to reel back with a shriek of pain. You turn to see Pelanthius standing nearby, firing a white beam of energy at the evil ghosts. A moment later, the Spectres shrivel into nothingness. Turn to **107**.

62

You sit on the deck and enjoy the view for several hours, but as evening draws in, you realise that Pelanthius has been absent all day. You presume that he is still reading or snoozing in his room, such is the way of Wizards.

When the sky begins to grow dark, Valantis passes the helm to a trusted crewman, then comes to join you. "The sea is a beautiful mistress," he mutters, gazing out across the waves. "It is a place of wonders, but it is not wise to turn your back on her. Storms often sweep upon us, and many colossal beasts haunt the ocean, just beneath her glittering surface. I have met many dangers out here, but the WindRunner is a fine vessel; she will carry us safely to Acura by tomorrow evening."

You ask Valantis to tell you some of his seafaring adventures, which he is only too happy to do. After a while of chatter, you follow him below deck to have supper with the sailors. You are greeted by a bowl of slop, but although it tastes revolting, it is actually quite nutritious. (Add two points to your **Life Force**.)

The hour has now grown late, so you decide to retire for the night, turn to **174**.

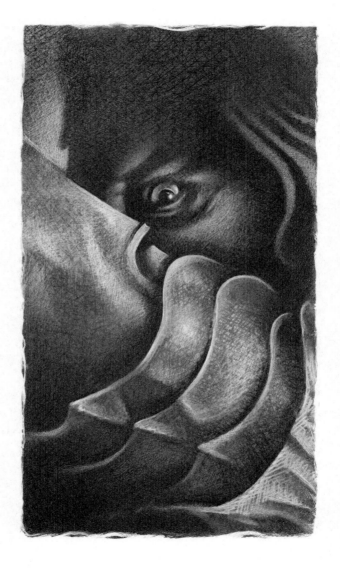

Illustration Opposite

You raise your sword and block the attack just in time. The Demon Stone suddenly glows, bolstering the King's strength, which enables him to inflict super-powerful blows. You duck and weave to avoid his initial attacks, then you are forced to strike back in retaliation.

(If you are using the guard's **Shortsword**, you will have a **-1 Damage** penalty to all of your weapon strikes for the duration of this fight. This is because the **Shortsword** is an inferior weapon, especially when pitched against Faranen's armour.)

THE CURSED KING

LIFE FORCE 9   STRIKING SPEED 8

Focus	Move	Damage
1	Pommel Smash	3
2-3	Slicing Blade	4
4-5	Downward Hack	4
6	Savage Sword Strike	5

If you survive this conflict, turn to **110**.

You check the wrecked buildings but the village is empty, so you progress onwards along the coastal trail. Before long, you leave the grassland and enter the foothills of the mountain. The ground slowly rises, turning lifeless and barren as you make your way up a snaking, rocky trail. As you press into a narrow valley, the troops grow quiet and nervous. You have entered the pass that leads all the way up to the mountain peak. Even though the sun is rising, the sky is growing gloomier. Clouds are massing overhead and the valley begins to slide into shadow. You can feel the presence of a great evil somewhere up ahead, and your skin begins to prickle.

A menacing cackle suddenly echoes over the top of the valley and several ghostly figures begin to sweep through the bellies of the dark clouds. The grisly Spectres are glowing with a strange blue aura, but they do not attack; they merely watch you, whilst gliding around beyond the reach of the Amossan archers.

Faranen grips his sword apprehensively. Up ahead, the valley curves to the right and you cannot see what lies beyond the bend.

If you advise Faranen to send a lone scout to look around the bend in the valley, turn to **18**.

If you advise him to push ahead with the whole army, turn to **124**.

The horrors are indeed scaling the wall, and a moment later you see a rotten, skeletal form dragging itself onto the walkway. The archers turn and loose a volley, but the ghastly figure ignores the thudding arrows. In an instant, it cuts down several archers with one swipe of its giant sword.

Gripping your weapon, you swiftly rush to their aid.

UNDEAD HORROR

LIFE FORCE 8   STRIKING SPEED 8

Focus	Move	Damage
1	**Raking Claws**	1
2-3	**Strangling Grasp**	1
4-5	**Stabbing Thrust**	2
6	**Ancient Blade Strike**	3

If you win, turn to **48**.

66

Glancing to your right, you see a scrawny, wild looking man springing at you with his rusty shortsword.

After fighting Blood-Gor, this fellow should be less of a challenge!

VILLAINOUS SWABBIE

LIFE FORCE 7   STRIKING SPEED 8

Focus	Move	Damage
1	Swinging Punch	1
2-3	Vicious Kick	1
4-5	Stabbing Blade	2
6	Devious Strike	2

If you win, turn to **44**.

67

You open the compartment, but it appears empty. You reach deep inside, where the shadows are thickest, and your fingers touch a cold object at the back. You have discovered a sapphire ring. It is not magical, but it is a delicate and beautiful item.

If you wish to take it, add the **Sapphire Ring** to your possessions, then turn to **371**.

68

For the remainder of the day you continue in a northerly direction. When the moon starts to rise, you see the coastal town of Port Kattaran glittering in the distance. You land on a grassy hill overlooking the settlement, then Pelanthius thanks Snowfire and tells him to return home.

"We must travel by ship from here," the Wizard tells you. "The skies to the east are ruled by the Great Eagles, who are large enough to steal a horse from a paddock, so it would be too dangerous for Snowfire to take us any further. We should still have time to succeed in our quest."

You certainly hope that he is right. You take out your map. "We need to get to Port Acura, on the island of Amossa," you exclaim. "It lies out on the Great Ocean. If we can reach it soon, we will be very close to our goal."

"Then we had best find ourselves a ship," says the Wizard. "Let us hope one is leaving soon from Port Kattaran."

With that in mind, you head down the hill. At the bottom is a deep waterway with a stone bridge. Several men have been hanged from the arched crossing, and their feet dangle in the gurgling water. The settlement looms on the far bank, and a large man, dressed all in black, stands guard at the town's gated entrance. He is holding a huge axe, and he waves you forward. "You may cross here, strangers," he says. "Wizards and warriors are welcome in Port Kattaran. I am Garand, the watchman. There is no toll for this bridge."

As you approach, you see that he is far bigger than you had first thought, and his face is covered in scars. He asks your business, and you tell him that you are looking for a ship that is bound for Port Acura.

"You should be in luck," he says, "but you would have to ask in town. I merely keep watch for Demons, among other threats. Speak to someone at the harbour, or make inquiries in the taverns."

If you ask about the poor souls that are hanging from the bridge, turn to **265**.

If you say no more, and head into town, turn to **298**.

You leap forward and drive the Dream-Sword into your enemy. A strange sound - like the agonised baying of inhuman voices - swirls out of the darkness. Crackling sparks of energy leap from the shadowy mass. Then a black arm with terrible claws takes shape and reaches towards you. You dodge the grasping hand, but you lose your footing on the uneven rocks and tumble backwards onto the ground. As you look up, you see that Evoka's head is already beginning to reform. Terrible eyes burn once more and you see that his reincarnation is progressing at an incredible pace. His outline is now twisted and deranged, with crooked limbs and segments which are still in the process of revival, but he is already halfway complete! Before you can get to your feet, a fork of black lightening erupts from his one, fully formed hand.

You are no longer blessed with the protection of Tirasel's armour, so you quickly raise the Dream-Sword in the desperate hope that you can deflect the blast.

You will have to be lucky to block the zigzagging magic.

If you possess an **Enchanted, Emerald Bracelet** or a **Glittering Bone Charm,** turn to **400.**

If not, turn to **186.**

You know that there is a manhole somewhere in Main Street, which leads down into the tunnels, so you head off in that direction. When you reach the street, you find the area heaving with people. Several flustered figures bump into you, running this way and that, and on three occasions you are almost knocked to the ground.

Suddenly, a great shadow looms over the crowd. People scream in horror, then a woman to your left almost faints with shock. A huge monstrosity is flying over the buildings, swooping close to the rooftops. It is an undead Dragon, but despite having bones for wings, it soars and sweeps through the sky with terrifying speed. The crowd surges and panics. Bodies crush into each other and you are almost elbowed in the face when a large man barrels past you.

The monster's bony tail clips the top of a nearby spire, smashing the roof into pieces, and huge blocks of stone tumble into the street towards the horrified crowd!

If you spring into action and do what you can to save the endangered townsfolk, turn to **177**.

If you run for cover, turn to **90**.

The stiff lever has not been used for a long age and it snaps off in your hand when you pull it! The crossbow fails to fire! Several foot-long splinters of razor sharp bone suddenly fly from the Dragon's mouth and shoot towards you, gleaming like sharpened spears. One of the projectiles tears into your thigh, causing you to cry out in pain. (Reduce your **Life Force** by three points!) If you are still alive, you have a split second to act before the Dragon tears into the machine with its giant claws!

You quickly grab the other lever. Turn to **89**.

The horse clears the tree, but when you look back you see that the swirling mist has drawn closer. A black mouth opens up in its fog-like body, then a terrible wind blasts from the dreadful maw. As the air rushes over you, a feverish sweat pours from your forehead and a soul rending pain tears deep within you.

(Reduce your **Life Force** by ten points!)

Suddenly, the horse finds a hidden reserve of energy and it begins to accelerate. The stallion speeds left and right along the branching trails and the black mist vanishes behind you into the shadow haunted woods. You have escaped for the moment, but you are beginning to feel fainter. Your very soul feels wounded, and your temperature has soared. Your heart suddenly spasms, then you pass out on the back of the steed.

Turn to **111**.

Suddenly, an explosive boom rattles over the valley, followed by a massive flash of green light on the upper slopes to your right. Looking towards the glare, you see a large figure clad in robes. It is the Demon, Golgorast, one of the foul trio who summoned Evoka! Your enemy has just detonated a small quantity of Elirium on the hillside, and the blast has set off a devastating avalanche. Huge boulders tumble down the incline, straight towards the Amossan ranks, and there is no time to avoid the landslide. With a look of dismay, Pelanthius thrusts his staff skyward and a blue dome of light flickers into existence around the entire army. Most of the boulders shatter as they strike the magical barrier, but the spell is not strong enough to halt all of the tumbling rocks.

If you have an **Amossan Shield**, you can protect yourself from the raining shards that make it through the Wizard's barrier. But if your **Amossan Shield** was recently destroyed, you will be struck and wounded by the deluge, and you must reduce your **Life Force** by three points.

If you are still alive, read on.

As the landslip rumbles to a halt, the Wizard's barrier flickers and vanishes. Pelanthius has managed to save the Amossan army, but it looks as if the effort has drained him.

Golgorast curses, then you hear his ghastly voice echoing from the hillside as he calls out your name.

"You may have survived my trap, human," he snarls, "but it matters not. Your end approaches, and nothing you can do will save you now. I would stay to watch your demise, but I have people to kill and plans to forge, so I will leave you to your fate."

He turns away with an evil laugh and vanishes over the lip of the valley. Every fibre in your body urges you to go after him, but a terrible noise, like bone against stone, suddenly rises into the air, halting you in your tracks. Turn to **183**.

74

As you charge forward, the dark figure suddenly rises into the air and hovers out of reach. His words rumble towards you like growling thunder, and you can hear the confidence in his voice. "I have been searching for you, Demon's Bane," says the evil figure. "Now, let us see how you fare against the wrath of Evoka!" Before you can act, a black tendril of energy leaps from his hand and strikes your body. You are instantly frozen to the spot, unable to move or speak. Several men break ranks and run to your aid, but your flesh and bones crumble into dust before they can reach you.

Your soul is absorbed into the body of your nemesis. And it will serve to increase his power.

75

The attacking army is relentless. The marching Skeletons keep coming, and there seems no end to the fighting. You fear that the defenders will not be able to hold out for much longer.

Suddenly, an axe is hurled towards you by one of the undead horrors. In the crush of people, you have no room to dodge.

You must roll one dice to see if luck is on your side.

If you roll a four or higher, turn to **99**.

If you roll a three or less, turn to **3**.

76

Before long you reach the end of the road. In front of you is an old building with a painted sign which reads: *Haynar's Weapon Shop*. As you head towards it, a large man in bearskin clothes exits the building. With a monstrously large axe strapped to his back, and muscled legs that are as thick as tree trunks, he looks every bit the barbarian. Long black hair hangs freely over his shoulders, and his jaw is brutishly square. As he walks past, he nods to you in greeting. "Good weapons in

Haynar's Shop," he says gruffly. "I travel here once a year just to visit it." He then thuds off to make his way out of town, back into the wilderness.

Any compliment from a barbarian is high praise indeed, so you head into the shop. As you walk inside, you are struck by the sheer volume of weapons on sale. Axes of all shapes and sizes hang from the walls, but you are most interested in the sword behind the counter. It is a fierce looking weapon, with a black blade that glitters as if made from a strange material.

"It's a mighty weapon, that one," says Haynar, the burly, bearded shop owner. "Its name is Night-Slayer, and it was forged in the Black-Cinian Mines, under the mountains far to the north."

Your eyes are also drawn to your right, where a finely made bow hangs from the wall. Both items have gained your interest, but the prices are high and the owner will not haggle.

The sword costs an eye watering **twenty Crimson Coins.** If you want to buy it, you will have to trade in your old weapon for **five Crimson Coins**, as per the shopkeeper's insistence. **Night-Slayer** will increase the **Damage** of your **Sweeping Blade** and **Heavy Sword Strike** by one point each.

The **Boar-Tusk Bow** has a price of **ten Coins**, and you should note that it comes with **five Black Tipped Arrows**.

When you are done here, you leave the shop and head back down the street. Turn to **198**.

As you step through the cave entrance, you are immediately struck by a great heat. You are on the bank of a bubbling lava lake, which is illuminating the whole cave with its red-hot glow. There is a dark rocky island at its centre, with a black oval shape hovering above it. The floating anomaly is nearly thirty feet tall and eight feet wide, with dark edges that are slowing moving and bending. You are looking at the gateway between worlds - the portal that links this world to the Land of the Dead - and you must destroy it as quickly as possible.

In the fiery light, you can see two bridges that lead to the island.

If you have the special ability of **Sixth Sense**, turn to **196**.

If not, you must choose from one of the following options:

If you want to cross the lake via the bridge to your left, turn to **28**.

If you want to cross the lake via the bridge to your right, turn to **123**.

With your last strike, your enemy collapses backwards, toppling a tree as it does so, then the beast lays silent. You rush over to check on Pelanthius, who looks ruffled and bruised, but fortunately he is not badly hurt. You pull him out of the bush where he landed and help him to tug the twigs and leaves from his beard.

"That beast was immune to my magic," he says. "If it hadn't been for you..."

"There is no need for thanks," you tell him. "In fact, had you not distracted the brute with your spell, I may well have been stomped on!"

Pelanthius scans the night-dark trees. "Moon Giants are notorious hoarders," he says, "and they never stray far from their lairs. We should take a quick look around, for there might be some useful loot nearby."

You decide to go along with this plan, and it is not long before you find a huge cave mouth in the slope of a heavily wooded hill. Within the dark lair, you discover a large number of shattered animal bones, and even the half mulched skeleton of an unfortunate adventurer. The dead man's backpack has been discarded nearby, so you take a look inside. You find **five Crimson Coins**, **four Black Tipped Arrows** and a **Small Fairy Statue** which is no bigger than your thumb.

The items will obviously be of no further use to the unfortunate explorer, so you take what you want before leaving.

As you head back towards the clearing, you find Snowfire waiting amongst the trees. He looks eager to escape this murky forest, so you clamber onto his back and swoop off into the dark sky. Turn to **105**.

You jump the stream, but you have not gone much further when a large branch grabs you around the waist and lifts you from your feet. Before you can think, you find yourself being pulled towards an ancient tree.

A ghastly mouth opens in the trunk, then you see a jagged mess of pointed teeth within the cavernous hole. Your writhe and kick, attempting to free yourself, but your enemy's grasp is too strong. With a curse, you quickly draw your sword and lash out at the monstrous abomination!

MUTANT TREE

LIFE FORCE 15   STRIKING SPEED 7

Focus	Move	Damage
1	Raking Branches	1
2-3	Crushing Embrace	2
4-5	Chomping Jaws	3
6	Gnashing Maw	3

If you win, you scramble onwards up the trail. Turn to **300**.

You stoop over the table and peer at the scattered objects. They are small clippings of worthless metal, fused together to form odd, humanoid shapes. You are unsure of their purpose. At any rate, they are of no value to you. Pushing them aside, you cast your eyes over a bundle of cloth that sits beneath the fading flame, and you find **three Crimson Coins** tucked inside. (If you wish to take the money, add it to your belongings.)

You should now pick an option which you have not yet chosen:

If you investigate the mysterious chalk markings, turn to **240**.

If you look inside the bowls, turn to **306**.

If you look closer at the stuffed birds, turn to **234**.

If you are ready to leave, turn to **129**.

81

Ugluk twists his body and manages to avoid the full force of your blow. Your knuckles glance the side of his head.

If you keep fighting, turn to **241**.

If you leap off the stage and admit defeat, turn to **169**.

82

You deflect most of the blades, but one pierces your body and flies straight through to the far side! To your amazement, the weapon leaves no mark, nor any sign of a wound, but the pain you suffer is very real indeed. The Spirit Dagger has pierced your soul, or at least that is how it feels, and a deep, agonizing sensation burns within you.

(Reduce your **Life Force** by three points!)

If you are still alive, turn to **164**.

83

The cottage door has been smashed down and the interior has been trashed. It is clear that the owners left in a hurry. A half-eaten bowl of soup still sits on a table, buzzing with flies, and a cracked water jug lies on the floor where the farmer's wife had been startled, dropped it and fled.

You check the rooms and discover a **Small Health Potion**, which you find on a bedside table. (If you take it, you may drink it at any time, even during combat. It will instantly increase your **Life Force** by five points.)

You follow Faranen into the adjacent barns, but there is nothing to see except for some farming equipment and a few bundles of hay.

"Looks like the area is clear after all," says one soldier, who is standing by your side. You nod in agreement, but just as you are about to leave, you hear a cracking sound nearby. As you glance back, the floorboards suddenly bend upwards and burst apart in a hail of splinters. Three monstrous forms explode from the ground. Their bodies are made entirely of bones, and their massive horned skulls have jaws that are lined with hundreds of sharp teeth. The undead Giant Earthworms have been summoned from their rest by the foul magic that is poisoning the land around the mountain. The lower halves of their bodies are submerged in the earth, but you are well within reach of their huge, lunging jaws.

These burrowing giants have not roamed the world since the prehistoric age, but they are as dangerous now as they ever were. You attack one enemy, whilst Faranen and his soldiers battle the others.

ANCIENT, SKELETAL EARTHWORM

LIFE FORCE   14   STRIKING SPEED   8

Focus	Move	Damage
1	Glancing Strike	1
2-3	Horned-Skull Smash	2
4-5	Monstrous Bite	3
6	Crushing Jaws	4

If you win, your other enemies have been smashed to splinters by the king and his men. Faranen's armour is dented and battle-scarred, but he has not been badly injured. Turn to **151**.

<h1 style="text-align:center">84</h1>

You settle into your swinging bunk and close your eyes. The ship's quiet creaking and swaying lulls you into a deep sleep, then you dream beneath the folds of your thin blanket.

As the vessel sails on, the temperature grows steadily colder. Frost begins to cling to the outside of the ship and the sails shiver in the late autumn wind.

(If you purchased a **Fur Coat** from a trader in RedBrook, you sleep well for the next few hours and you may increase your **Life Force** by one point. If you are not wearing a **Fur Coat**, you toss and turn in your hammock and you become freezing cold, hence you must *reduce* your **Life Force** by one point. If you are still alive, read on.)

Late in the night, you are woken by a sudden lurching which nearly throws you from your bunk. Opening your eyes, you gaze out through a porthole and see that a wild storm is taking place. The boat is leaning this way and that, and the sea looks swollen and savage in the moonlight. Above the call of the wind, you think you can hear voices calling for help. You decide to investigate, so you walk through the rocking ship until you come to the open hatchway that leads up to the deck. As you poke your head through the opening, you see several crew members running around in a panic. Wind and rain lashes your face, but through the storm you can see a distant, dark shape beating through the water. It is a Pirate ship, and it is closing in fast. The crew on your vessel are arming themselves with shortswords, large iron hooks and whatever makeshift weapons they can find.

During your sea voyage, have you encountered any **abandoned vessels**?

If so, turn to **182**.

If not, turn to **100**.

85

The soldier - whose name is Taisun - offers to show you the view from the battlements. When you get there, it is too dark to see much beyond the city walls. The moon is riding high and the black outline of The Claw is silhouetted in the distance. Taisun informs you that you are only three miles from the foot of the mountain. "Several villages lay between us and the mountain," he says, "but those settlements have been overrun by shuffling, skeletal beings, which is why everyone has fled to the city."

"Is there any way that a lone warrior could sneak up the mountain and reach the gateway?" you ask.

The guard shakes his head. "A person might make it to the foot of the mountain, but there is no way that a lone adventurer could get further than that. Our scouts have already tried. As I said, nightmarish figures are everywhere on those slopes, and they have gathered in vast numbers."

"Then we have no choice but to confront King

Faranen," says Pelanthius. "We must convince him to mobilise his army."

"You speak wisely," says Taisun, "but as I told you, I do not believe that the king wishes to assault the mountain. Otherwise, he would have given the order already. Maybe he fears the army of bones, or maybe he is thinking up a different plan... I simply cannot say."

"I will go and speak with him," you say. "Rest assured, I will find a way to end this madness."

Turn to **157**.

86

The Amossans have suffered many casualties but, despite the odds, they appear to be winning the fight. Their confidence has remained strong and their skill in combat is outshining the enemy's. The undead horde starts to crumble under the onslaught and their numbers begin to dwindle. Soon, a cluster of just fifty Skeletons remain, crowded together in a tightly packed group. You smash your way into the heart of their ranks, leaving a wreckage of bones in your wake, and your comrades quickly follow you into the depths of the fray. A final, fierce battle erupts. Swords swish and axes slam with brutal force into the sturdy Amossan shields. Several men fall in the skirmish but, after a few minutes, the final abominations are reduced to a pile of shattered remnants. You quickly scan the battlefield, but not a single opponent remains.

Across the valley, many brave men lie upon the ground, stricken and wounded. You spot Faranen amongst them, slumped against a rock with a pained look on his face. His breastplate has been dented by a savage spear strike, but his injuries are not fatal. As you move towards him, you see that Pelanthius is already kneeling beside him. The old Wizard is uninjured, but he looks weary and out of breath.

"The evil in this valley has been crushed," says Faranen, "but I am too wounded to continue. You must go with the Wizard and follow the gorge to the summit of the mountain. Our victory is not secured until the gateway is destroyed!"

A group of men, around forty in total, step forward and offer to help you. The rest are too badly injured to continue.

If you tell Pelanthius to stay and help the wounded, whilst you set off with the warriors, turn to **121**.

If you would rather Pelanthius joined you on the final stage of your quest, turn to **43**.

87

"I have come to visit my friend who lives in the nearby forest," you tell him. "He was not at home when I arrived. Maybe you know of him, or have seen him recently?"

The man's eyes show a sudden hint of fear. "You mean the old Wizard, Moras Kazal?"

At the mention of his name, several people stop talking and look around with a shiver of dread.

The bartender lowers his voice. "I wouldn't visit Moras Kazal if I were you," he says. "He used to be a good man, but his obsession with potion making led to his downfall. He would test all of his potions on himself, to ensure their safety before selling them to the townsfolk. But his last concoction had an adverse effect on him. He was afflicted by a sudden madness. I would not advise going to that place, not unless you are looking for trouble."

You are gravely disturbed by what you have learnt, but you thank the barman for his information.

If you wish to leave the tavern immediately to warn Pelanthius about this worrying turn of events, turn to **198**.

If you would rather press the man for more information, turn to **166**.

88

"Forgive me," says Pelanthius. "You have been through a great deal these past days and you are clearly weary. Let me see what I can do to help." He waves his hand through the air whilst muttering a few words, then he gently taps you on the nose with the end of his staff.

"There, how do you feel now?" he asks.

Tiny, golden sparkles drift briefly in the air before you, then a tingling sensation runs the length of your body.

(Increase your **Life Force** by four points.)

You feel much more alert, so you thank the Wizard and tell him that his spell has worked.

"Good," he says with a smile. "I can only cast that spell once per season, so be careful and look after yourself from here on. Now follow me! We cannot dally any longer." Turn to **195**.

89

You yank the lever just in time, then a huge, tightly wound cog spins free. Your seat shudders violently as a giant, rusty arrow is fired out of the lower part of the mechanism. The shaft of the projectile is at least twenty feet long and the arrowhead is a massive lump of steel which probably weighs more than a ton.

The Dragon arches upwards in an attempt to avoid your attack, but the arrow crashes into its side.

Roll one dice to see if luck is with you.

If you roll a one or a two, turn to **6**.

If you roll a three or higher, turn to **95**.

90

As you push your way through the chaos, a man bumps into you and knocks you from your feet. Before you can leap up, a huge slab of rock spirals out of the sky and hits the ground to your left, exploding into sharp fragments. You feel a tearing pain as a piece of stone buries into your shoulder, lodging in the muscle. You pull it out and press your hand against the wound to stem the bleeding.

(Reduce your **Life Force** by two points.)

As the crowd flees into the offshoots and narrow lanes, you hear an eerie wail. It is the sound of air shrieking through the Dragon's ribcage, as the monster circles round for another attack. You suddenly spot the opening to the sewers, so you race towards it.

Turn to **292**.

A savage battle instantly erupts along the front line. A wretched figure leaps towards you, but you obliterate its skull with the crushing sweep of your sword. The Skeleton falls apart and clatters to the ground. Your opponents are clearly fragile, but in such heavy numbers they will prove immensely dangerous. Three more waves pour in through the breach, but they are brutally destroyed by the line of defenders. However, the battle is about to get tougher.

A group of Skeletons, clad in chain mail, now lurch in through the wrecked gate. Each nightmarish figure is twice the height of a full-grown man, with skulls that are protected by glittering helms of spiked, black iron. These wretched things will prove harder to slay than the last batch of aggressors and, in the swirling chaos, you are forced to take on two of them at once.

ANCIENT WARRIORS

LIFE FORCE   12   STRIKING SPEED   8

Focus	Move	Damage
1	**Claws of Jagged Bone**	1
2-3	**Pommel Slam**	2
4-5	**Thrusting Sword**	3
6	**Sweeping Axe**	3

If you win, turn to **21**.

A secret door slides open in the wall. The entrance is thick with cobwebs, and musty air drifts out of the opening. You cautiously edge into the shadows, and you discover a cramped little room with a block of stone at its centre. Resting on the stone is a crooked wand. You can feel a terrible power emanating from it, and your skin prickles as you pick it up. You have no idea how to use this weapon, but you suspect that it would be deadly in the hands of a Witch.

If you want to take it, add the **Black-Wood Wand** to your list of possessions. There is nothing else in here, so you return to the main living room. The secret door slides shut behind you.

Turn to page **148** and pick an option that you have not yet chosen.

"RedBrook is not a huge place," says the Wizard, "so it shouldn't be too difficult to find him. Besides, a visit to the town could come in useful. There are a surprising number of shops that are tucked away in the cobbled lanes, so we might pick up a few bargains that could help us on our quest."

The Wizard tells Snowfire to wait by Kazal's tower, then he heads towards the edge of the clearing.

You follow him along a narrow track which winds down a steep, wooded slope. The ground eventually levels out, and you are forced to jump a small stream before exiting the wood. You soon find yourself at the border of a quaint town, with old stone buildings and winding streets. People mill about in different directions, paying little interest to your arrival.

"If we split up, we will be able to explore the settlement in less time," says Pelanthius. "Let us meet back in the town square in one hour." You agree to his suggestion, then you prepare to part ways.

If you are travelling in the company of a **Toad**, turn to **192** immediately.

If not, you may choose from one of the following options.

If you head to The Wishing Well Tavern, to ask if anyone has information about Kazal, turn to **101**.

If you want to investigate Beggar's Lane, turn to **54**.

If you want to head for Lore Street, turn to **27**.

If you want to explore Sword Street, turn to **38**.

94

The stallion clears the tree by the scantest of margins, its hooves clipping the bark before thumping back onto the path. You glance over your shoulder. The mist is now dangerously close, and it is sucking the life out of everything around it. The nearby trees wither and die, and their branches crumble into ash. Your enemy's deadly aura begins to affect you, and a searing pain rips into your body. Sweat pours from your forehead, and it feels as if your soul is dying.

(Reduce your **Life Force** by eight points!)

You feel faint, but you manage to keep your grip on the reigns. Suddenly, the horse begins to accelerate, as if it has found a hidden reserve of energy. The stallion speeds left and right along branching trails, then the mist vanishes into the woods behind you. You have escaped for the moment, but you are beginning to feel fainter. Your heart suddenly spasms, then you pass out on the back of the steed.

Turn to **111**.

95

The lump of iron tears through the Dragon's ribcage and obliterates a huge swathe of its spine, ripping its skeleton in two. The beast falls apart in mid-air, then the detached skull spirals downwards, just missing the tower upon which you are perched. The rest of the bones tumble into the streets and smash through the rooftops of several houses.

Turn to **175**.

After a short while you come to a dead end, but all is not as it seems. You search around and soon discover a secret door, cunningly concealed at the end of the passage. You drag it open and step through into a warm, dimly lit room. You see vials of bubbling liquid, strange apparatus, and glittering potions everywhere. You have found Kazal's secret laboratory, and you can see that his experiments were ongoing right up until the hour before his death. As you survey the cluttered scene, something catches your eye. A green bottle sits alone from the others, balancing precariously on the corner of a desk. It is sitting atop a batch of explanatory notes. (The sealed bottle is filled with a corrosive liquid that can burn through armour, flesh and bone. If you wish to take it, you should add **Kazal's Potion of Pain** to your list of possessions. At any time during close combat, you may hurl it at an enemy; it will automatically deal five points of damage to your opponent's **Life Force**. If and when you use it, remove it from your Character Sheet.)

Pelanthius advises you to leave the other bottles alone, as they are all unlabelled and you have no clue as to what might be in them. You make your way out of the room and return to the corridor. Turn to **26**.

97

You look up and see that the sky is growing red. The sun is setting and the clouds have faded into purple hues. Pelanthius is due to meet you soon, so you sit on the plinth of a sundial and wait for him. After half an hour there is still no sign of the old Wizard. The moon begins to rise and you start to grow worried. It occurs to you that he might have returned to the tower early, so you leave the square and make your way back to the edge of the wood. As you approach the tree line, you see two children playing with stones nearby.

If you have visited the Wishing Well Tavern, turn to **35**.

If you have not, turn to **152**.

98

To your horror, the enemy numbers start to swell around you as more and more ghastly figures flood onto the walkway. Despite their best efforts, the defence begins to crumble against the onslaught. You look around for reinforcements, and you are relieved to see a large unit of heavily armoured men heading across the courtyard. As they race onto the ramparts, you see that each man is armed with a huge war hammer. They tear into the enemy's ranks with bone-shattering force, and in a few minutes they have fought their way across to you. A large warrior with a wild red beard appears at your side, and you work together to batter a number of nightmarish figures from the walkway. You have soon regained control of the ramparts, and the climbing monstrosities have all been obliterated. The main gate is still standing, but it remains under heavy assault and you have no time to relax. You suddenly notice a glittering shape, flying through the sky towards the town. It is quite some distance away, but it is approaching fast. People gaze in horror and disbelief as they recognise it, for it is the skeletal remains of a long dead Dragon, reanimated by a spell of immeasurable power.

The bearded warrior, whose name is Clayton, is still standing at your side. "What madness is this?!" he cries. "That thing looks savage enough to tear a hole right through this wall."

"We have to slay it before it reaches the town," you tell him.

Clayton nods. "I have an idea. I can't guarantee that it will work, but it's the only plan I can think of. Come, I'm going to need your help." He quickly rushes off.

If you follow him, turn to **29**.

If you decide to flee the besieged town, by escaping through the sewers, turn to **70**.

The weapon misses you and spins over the heads of the other defenders, but you have barely breathed a sigh of relief when your heart leaps with horror. An undead horse charges through the gate, clad in ancient armour, and ridden by a terrible Skeleton with flaming eyes.

It storms towards the line of men, in a bid to smash its way through their ranks! Turn to **144**.

100
Illustration Opposite

Peering from the hatchway, you watch as the ship draws nearer. The ominous vessel is soon very close, and the Pirates line the deck in anticipation. Just as they are about to leap from their ship to yours, they are suddenly distracted by something in the water. To your surprise, the villainous crew start to yell and panic, then the enemy ship jerks backwards, away from the WindRunner. You notice a monstrous shape in the rolling sea, with huge, tentacle-like arms! The enormous creature has gripped the enemy vessel, and you can hear the creak of timbers as the monster begins to crush the ship's hull. The Pirates scramble to fight off their assailant, but in just a few moments the ship is dragged under the waves, into the gigantic mouth of the murderous Sea Titan.

The merchant sailors begin to cheer with delight, but their relief soon turns to horror. The beast is still hungry, and its long arms are now reaching towards the WindRunner! Vast tentacles, twice as thick as tree trunks, begin to wrap around your vessel. Valantis runs past you, barking orders at his crew. "Attack its arms!" he roars. "Cut us free, before that thing drags us down!"

You decide that the time has come to act. Sword in hand, you clamber onto the rainwashed deck. To your left, several crewmen hack into one of the tentacles, but they quickly stumble backwards in agony, their arms and faces burnt by the creature's acidic blood.

One of the tentacles is moving towards the mast. You have to stop it! If you have a **Bow** and **Arrow**, and want to fire at the tentacle from a safe distance, turn to **296**.

If you leap forward with your sword, turn to **386**.

The Wishing Well Tavern is located near the edge of town. A line of smoke drifts lazily from its crooked chimney, and you can hear chatter floating out through the window. A golden glow is in the sky, and you realise that the evening is drawing in. You push open the door and step into a large room with a wood beamed ceiling. A fireplace has recently been lit, and the warmth is inviting. Several people are talking at round tables, and a young woman is leaning by the fireplace with a distant look in her eyes, plucking soulfully on a string instrument.

"Welcome, stranger," says a deep voice. You turn to see a portly fellow standing behind the bar. "What will yer be drinking on this fine evening?" he asks. "Will it be a mug of Wishing Well Brew, a goblet of Rot-Wood Black Sap, or some Dragon's Forge ale?"

If you ask for his recommendation, turn to **139**.

If you tell him that you are not here to drink and that you are seeking information, turn to **87**.

You react just in time. The magical beam sweeps over your head and strikes the wall behind you, leaving hissing burn marks in the stone. With a curse, Kazal quickly waves his staff and mutters the words to another spell.

Before you can act, a gust of wind lifts you from your feet and hurls you across the room, slamming you into the opposite wall.

Roll one dice to see if luck is on your side.

If you roll a three or less, your head strikes the stone and you must reduce your **Life Force** by two points.

If you are lucky enough to roll a four or higher, you are uninjured by the impact.

If you survive Kazal's *Wind Spell*, he quickly levels his staff, then a second beam of energy shoots towards you! Turn to **37**.

The city is vast, and it takes another fifteen minutes before you reach your destination. The grand building is located at the heart of the sprawling city, with domed towers and broad white steps leading up to a set of double doors. The main entrance is sealed, and many guards in plumed helmets stand before it. Each sentinel is armed with an ornate spear, and their expressions are stoic. As you approach, they order you to come no closer. "Be away with you," says one of the men. "The ruler of Amossa has given orders that he is not to be disturbed."

If you tell the guard that you have important news for the king, regarding the troubles that have beset this land, turn to **30**.

If you would rather stay quiet and let Pelanthius do the talking, turn to **117**.

104

The creature hollers with disappointment, then it hurls four coins at you, which include the two that you gave him. (Increase your money accordingly.)

The contest is now over, the table is in ruins, and the crowd begin to disperse into the various lanes that lead from the courtyard. As they do so, you overhear two men talking about Port Acura. They leave down a side turning called Dead Man's Walk, but they have disappeared by the time you get there.

If you explore the turning, turn to **286**.

If you leave via a different lane, and follow the signs towards the harbour, turn to **204**.

Before long, you find yourself surrounded by a murky storm. Thunder rattles, and sparks of lightening illuminate the brooding darkness. You have entered a great sea of clouds that has gathered across Kostaria, so you are unlikely to see the crows again.

As the hours pass, the wind builds, pushing you along at an incredible speed. The clouds swirl and crash, writhing in a chaotic dance, whilst hammering the land with icy rain.

"How easy it would be, to become lost in such a place," you call, and the Wizard nods in agreement.

"Without Kazal's compass, we would end up flying in circles for days," says Pelanthius, gripping tightly to the small object. "The storms in this region sometimes stretch for hundreds of miles, east to west. There is no way around them, but thanks to this artefact we should find our way through. Keep a grip on me. It is a long way down, and the wind up here is bitter and merciless."

You fly onwards for a whole day and night, and you are left shivering from the cold. (Unless you are wearing a fur coat, you must reduce your **Life Force** by three points due to the freezing conditions.)

Finally, on a cold, blustery morning, you break through to the far side of the grim clouds. The wind eases, and you are relieved to see the dawning sun. Below, white ocean waves beat against a line of cliffs, and darting seabirds soar on the brisk currents. Hastened by the storm's fury, you have covered a huge distance, but your mount is exhausted and in need of rest.

You set down on top of a grassy cliff and, whilst Snowfire slumbers, you gather some wild pickings from the hilltop. You feel utterly famished, but you soon find enough food for both you and Pelanthius. (If you have a book named **Healing Plants and Where to Find Them**, you may increase your **Life Force** by four points. If not, your **Life Force** is increased by two points instead, thanks to your breakfast.)

After the meal, you sleep briefly in the grass alongside Snowfire, then you set off once more.

Turn to **68**.

106

You walk onwards. After a while you come to a dark alley with an open, crooked door at its end. A sign above the entrance bids you to enter, so you warily step inside.

In front of you, a crowd is gathered around a raised wooden platform, upon which a huge man is standing. There is an unconscious body at his feet, and you realise that you have walked into a fighter's den. This is a seedy, rough looking place, and money exchanges hands at a counter where bets are placed.

Ugluk, the current champion, is flexing his muscles on stage. He is close to eight feet tall, wearing nothing but some loose-fitting trousers. His hairy chest and arms are immense with muscle, and his square jaw is enormous. Although he looks human, his teeth are suspiciously pointed and his eyes gleam with a monstrous ferocity. You suspect that he is a Half-Ogre. When he calls out for a new challenger, his voice sounds inhumanly deep. "I'll give ten coins to anyone who can beat me," he roars. "No weapons allowed. This is hand-to-hand combat."

No one is quick to accept his offer. He steps to the edge of the platform and, after scanning the crowd, he singles you out by pointing at you with his chunky finger. "What about you, newcomer? Fancy your luck?"

If you agree to his challenge, turn to **34**.

If you refuse, you may leave the building and continue down the street: turn to **198**.

107

The battle has now been raging for some time.

Roll two dice and combine them to determine the morale of the Amossan troops. If you stopped the Giant from attacking King Faranen, add seven to the total.

If the final figure is four or less, turn to **328**.

If the final figure is five to twelve, turn to **393**.

If the final figure is thirteen or higher, turn to **86**.

108

You step into the room. Shelves, bearing rows of potions, fill the right-hand wall, and a long desk with bubbling equipment sits at the back. The owner, a thin man in black robes, is searching a set of drawers to your left, whilst grumbling about some missing ingredients.

If you speak to him, turn to **340**.

If you leave him to his business, whilst you browse the merchandise, turn to **311**.

109

You are about to turn away when you notice a dark crystal on a black necklace, resting on the edge of the bookshelf. Stars and galaxies seem to glitter in the crystalline depths, and you feel strangely drawn to the mysterious artefact.

If you wish to take it, add the **Black Crystal Necklace** to your list of possessions, then turn to page **148** and pick an option that you have not yet chosen.

110

Your opponent falls to the ground, but as he hits the floor, you hear a dreamlike whispering coming from the stone around his neck. The king's wounds suddenly heal, then his eyes open, and he comes up upon his feet once more.

Gripping his sword, the revived King advances towards you.

"What evil witchcraft is this?!" cries the guard, who has woken from his coma. "Cast away that stone, my Lord. It has corrupted you!" The soldier gets to his feet and attempts to tear the artefact from Faranen's neck, but the king knocks him to the ground with a mighty strike.

You realise that in order to defeat Faranen, you will have to destroy the cursed Demon Stone. With bold intentions, you surge forward and swipe at it with your sword. It is a small target, and because it is swinging wildly from his neck, your aim will have to be perfect in order to hit it.

Roll one dice to see if luck is on your side. If you are wearing an **Enchanted, Emerald Bracelet** or a **Glittering Bone Charm,** add one to the number rolled.

If the total is four or less: your blade misses the Demon Stone, then Faranen knocks you back with the pommel of his sword, doing one point of damage to your **Life Force**.

You must keep repeating this process until you get a total that is five or higher, at which point you should turn to **135**.

You wake slowly. The stallion has halted and a night sky looms overhead. You are slumped across the back of the horse, and you see that the big animal has carried you high onto the slope of a mountain. You can see the distant shape of the pine forest below, and its outline looks dark and sinister under the wan light of the moon. Fortunately, there is no sign of your enemy.

As you scan your surroundings, you notice a small, old woman sitting on a nearby boulder. She is bent over with a hunched back, with long hair covering all but her crooked nose. She has the look of a Witch about her, so you quickly reach for your sword.

"Do not fear me," she croaks. "I have been waiting for you to regain consciousness. I am not here to do you any harm."

Your eyes narrow and you keep your hand readily on the hilt of your sword.

"You are wise to be cautious of me," she says. "Usually I would have dragged you off and put you into my pot while you slept, but today I am not here to hurt you." She shuffles to her feet and stares up at you with her beady eyes. "A foul warlord attacked you this morning, and make no mistake, you *will* see him again. Fortunately for you, he is my enemy too, and thus it makes sense for me to aid you. I cast a spell of strength on your horse, to help it outrun the evil mist in the pine wood. Had I not done so, you would certainly have been slain."

"I am not sure whether to believe you," you say. "I have had dealings with your kind before, and it has always ended in treachery. If you speak the truth, then tell me this: who was the tyrant who attacked Mosal, and why was he so intent on killing me?"

"His name is Evoka," she answers, "and he is a powerful God. All those with an evil heart must meet him one day, for it is he who rules over the Land of the Dead, where wicked souls are damned to dwell for eternity. Once upon a time, he was the king of the moonlit sky, but his evil deeds came to the attention of the other Gods, so they banished him into the Underworld, where he was cursed to rule forever more. For an ageless time he dreamt of returning to the Land of the Living. However, until recently, there was no way for him to escape the black pits of his lightless prison."

"Then how *did* he escape?" you ask. "And you have still not answered my other question: what does this creature want with *me*?"

"I will answer your questions," says the Witch, "but first you must follow me up the mountain. It is not safe to talk here, under the eyes of the world."

You are ill at ease with this sinister alliance, but you do as she asks.

You guide the horse up the rocky slope until you come to a small, stone hut, which has been disguised as a boulder. It has a black door and a crooked chimney, and there are no windows that you can see. You watch as the Witch mutters a password under her breath, then the door swings open and yellow light shines out through the gap. You hear the sound of a bubbling pot within.

"Come in," she says. "We do not have much time and there is a lot to discuss." She shuffles through the doorway and you hear her clattering around inside the dwelling.

With your hand still resting on the hilt of your sword, you dismount and step cautiously through the entrance.

Turn to **143**.

112

You have an uneasy feeling about this place. A weight of sadness lingers in the air, as if the dwelling is haunted by lost souls.

"Many people have died here," you mutter aloud, without meaning to.

The old woman shakes her head. "Your senses deceive you," she says, quietly. "But there is some truth to your words." You feel the air growing colder, and her eyes glitter darkly. "I commune with the Spirit Winds," she says. "It is they who whisper the secrets of the future, and whose breathless voices drift in the shadows, for only me to hear." She lights a black candle in front of her, scatters several cat bones onto the tabletop, then asks you for a single crimson coin.

You pause.

"Does your heart yearn to flee, for fear of what it might learn?" she asks.

If you put a coin onto the table, remove it from your belongings and turn to **215**.

If you make your excuses and leave, turn to **264**.

Even Pelanthius is affected by the dark magic that lingers here. He casts a spell in an attempt to protect the group, but nothing he does seems to work. He collapses on the floor, breathless and pale, suffocating and in terrible pain. For reasons that you do not understand, you alone are unaffected by the strange forces that are at work here. You grab Pelanthius and drag him backwards. As you pull him down the slope, you see that his pain is easing. The men follow your lead and crawl to the bottom of the steps. Here their symptoms vanish and they get to their feet. It is clear that none of them will be able to reach the summit. You will have to complete the last stage of your journey alone.

You tell your comrades to stay where they are, whilst assuring them that you will return soon. Pelanthius looks worried, but there is no choice in the matter. You clutch your weapon and ascend the steps alone.

Turn to **77**.

The man is swift indeed, and he leads you on a wild pursuit through the back alleys of the town. Eventually you lose sight of him as he sweeps around a corner. As you chase round the bend, you are greeted by a nasty surprise. The grinning Thief is waiting with two large thugs. You draw your sword as they advance towards you.

TRIO OF THIEVES

LIFE FORCE 16   STRIKING SPEED 8

Focus	Move	Damage
1	Wild Punch	1
2-3	Elbow To The Face	1
4-5	Sweeping Bat	2
6	Stabbing Dagger	2

If you win, turn to **367**.

115

Creeping downwards, you enter a square chamber. A flickering candle, surrounded by trinkets, sits on a black table at the heart of the room. Amidst the deep shadows and wan light, you see strange chalk markings on the floor, and stuffed birds hanging from the low ceiling. Shelves line the walls, filled with a collection of bowls, and the room has a creepy atmosphere.

If you investigate the chalk markings, turn to **240**.

If you examine the trinkets on the table, turn to **80**.

If you would rather look inside the bowls, turn to **306**.

If you decide to get out of this place and return to the ship, turn to **338**.

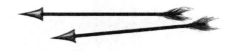

You sit on the deck and enjoy the view for several hours, but as evening draws in, you realise that Pelanthius has been absent all day. You presume that he is still reading or snoozing in his room, such is the way of Wizards.

When the sky begins to grow dark, Valantis passes the helm to a trusted crewman, then comes to join you. "The sea is a beautiful mistress," he mutters, gazing out across the waves. "It is a place of wonders, but it is not wise to turn your back on her. Storms often sweep upon us, and many colossal beasts haunt the ocean, just beneath her glittering surface. I have met many dangers out here, but the WindRunner is a fine vessel. She will carry us safely to Acura by tomorrow evening."

You ask Valantis to tell you some of his seafaring adventures, which he is only too happy to do. After a while of chatter, you follow him below deck to have supper with the sailors. You are greeted by a bowl of slop, but although it tastes revolting, it is actually quite nutritious.

(Add two points to your **Life Force**.)

After you have finished, Valantis invites you to join him for a game of dice, but only if you possess some coins to gamble with.

If you accept his invite, turn to **156**.

If you decline and retire for the night, turn to **174**.

"I am the Head of the Wizard's Council," Pelanthius exclaims. "Step aside and let us pass."

"The Head of the Wizard's Council?" laughs the guard. "You look nothing more than an old man to me. Now move along, Grey Beard, before I grow tired of your presence."

The Wizard's nose twitches with annoyance. "You are testing my patience," he warns. "Only a fool would speak to a Wizard in such a manner. Now, step aside, or I shall teach you a lesson that you are unlikely to forget!"

The guard grips his spear in a steadfast manner, then Pelanthius's hand tightens around his staff. You have a feeling that trouble is brewing, so you quickly intervene.

Turn to **30**.

Your journey to Port Acura was not without its dangers, but you are relieved to have reached it safely. As you pass into the moonlit bay, you see a group of grim-faced soldiers waiting for you by a jetty. They are carrying torches and their swords are drawn, but they are not hostile. Port Acura seems very quiet indeed and the buildings by the quay look dark and empty. You realise that the lights you saw earlier were nothing more than the torches carried by the soldiers. There are no other signs of life in the whole area.

"Welcome, travellers," says one of the soldiers, in a stern voice. "We noticed you approaching from the mainland and it looked liked your vessel was in trouble, so we came down to the dock to meet you."

"It has been a bleak journey," acknowledges a sailor, "our ship was damaged in a battle, but we made it through." He looks around at the shadowy port. "What happened here?" he asks. "Port Acura was always a bustling place, even in the darkling hours."

"The area has been evacuated," answers the soldier. "All its inhabitants have been moved to the walled city of Amossa, a miles walk from here, beyond the sea cliffs. Shadows of evil have descended upon this land. If you want to know more, you had best come to the city with us, as it is not safe to linger out here by the bay."

You press him for more information, and the soldier's eyes look dark and troubled. "Some weeks ago, a flickering doorway opened up on the slopes of a nearby mountain. At first we did not know what to make of it, but we soon learnt that it was a portal to another world! A terrible darkness has been pouring from it, and a legion of undead creatures now stalks this land."

A strange, dreadful moan suddenly drifts up over the bay, echoing through the darkness like an omen of doom.

"Sounds like more rotting horrors are not far away," spits a second soldier. "Come, let us get back to the city, before we are ambushed."

You decide to follow the soldiers, in the hope of gathering more information. Turn to **45**.

Illustration Opposite

The Amossans attempt to close the gap in their shield wall, but they are unable to do so. Skeletal figures surge in amongst the soldiers, creating a chaotic scene of violent bloodshed. All around, swords sweep and axes slash, then the noise of the conflict becomes almost deafening.

Suddenly, a huge skeletal creature smashes up out of the ground to your left. Several people are knocked off of their feet, and your horse rears up in the chaos. You are being attacked by the undead remnants of a Giant Earthworm. It is a destructive beast of monstrous proportions, and you have no choice but to fight it. (You can immediately reduce your enemy's **Life Force** by five points, as the nearby soldiers are frantically hacking at it with their swords.)

GIANT, SKELETAL EARTHWORM
LIFE FORCE   15   STRIKING SPEED   8

Focus	Move	Damage
1	Glancing Strike	2
2-3	Horned Skull Smash	3
4-5	Crushing Bite	4
6	Chomping Frenzy	5

If you win, turn to **315**.

You clamber into your bunk and fall asleep almost instantly. When you wake, seven hours later, you find that the ship is already underway. You head up onto the deck and see Valantis standing at the wheel. His smile is broad, and his eyes look content.

"Warm taverns and strong ale are always a welcome distraction," he says, "but it is good to be riding the waves again."

You look past the stern, and you see Port Kattaran slowly shrinking into the distance. Vast, blue water lies ahead, and you know that you will not see land again for some time. As you watch the rolling waves, spray comes up over the deck, and you can taste the salt in the air.

"Your friend, the Wizard, paid a decent price for your bunks," says Valantis, "but he was very secretive as to his reasons for going to Port Acura. What brings you out onto the Great Ocean? Not that it is any of my business."

You do not yet know whether to trust this old sea dog, so you decide to change the subject. "A reasonable question," you acknowledge. "But you are quite right: it is none of your business."

Valantis guffaws. "Very well," he says. "I like to hear it as it is."

The ship sails on, into the vast ocean. Roll one dice to see what random events the day has in store for you.

If you roll a one, a two or a three, turn to **62**.

If you roll a four, a five or a six, turn to **116**.

Because of your decision to leave Pelanthius behind, the journey ahead might prove more dangerous. However, it was a choice worthy of a hero, and your valiance has not gone unnoticed. The soldiers pledge to protect you, come death or glory, and they gather to your side with their swords drawn. You say your farewells to Pelanthius, then you set off up the shadowy gorge.

Hours pass as you gradually make your way high above the world. The soldiers, who are clad in heavy armour, start to grow weary, but they do not grumble, and they continue to follow you with loyal resolve. The further you go, the darker the world seems to get. This is not because of the time of day, but because you are now pushing up into grey, brooding cloud. An hour before sundown, you come upon a narrow set of steps that have been cut into the rock.

"The steps of Mantium," says a half-breathless soldier. "They were cut into the mountain long ago, by the old kings of Amossa. We are not far from the top now, not far from that ghastly portal."

The soldier is right. You can sense a strange energy coming from somewhere ahead, and it feels like the presence of foul magic.

A gust of wind suddenly sweeps the slope, thinning the cloud. You can now see that the steps are ascending towards a large opening in the rock face. You have a feeling that the gateway lies within the heart of the mountain, so you boldly head towards the entrance.

Turn to **158**.

122

As you explain your tale, the guard's eyes slowly widen. By the time you have finished, he looks enraptured. "You are a stranger to this land," he says, "and as such, I am not sure whether to trust you. But I think the king should hear your tale for himself, in case you are telling the truth. Faranen will not be pleased at being disturbed; his mood has been stormy of late, so your grey bearded friend will have to stay here. The fewer people who come with me, the better." You nod in agreement, then the guard leads you up the steps.

Turn to **10**.

123

As you move across the bridge, the lava bubbles and churns in slow, circular currents. You dodge past the spitting blobs of molten fire which fall, hissing onto the path. And then you are at the edge of the island. It is a large mound of dark rock which rises to a sharp peak, where the grim portal hovers. As you step onto the bank, the gateway suddenly flickers and expands. Something within the portal has sensed your presence, and you see a huge, terrible shape forming within the black fissure!

A dreadful figure steps from the opening, and as it puts its first foot onto the ground, the mountain trembles with fear. The lava swirls and spits with greater fury, as if acknowledging the presence of a supreme evil.

Your nemesis, Evoka, stands before you. At the sight of him, your heart pounds in your chest and your veins rush with adrenaline. His tall, black form is humanoid, but his outline seems to change and bend with ethereal qualities. One moment he has two arms, then three, then only one. Beneath his crown, countless eyes burn like fire in the pit of his face, and twisted mouths appear and disappear in an ever-shifting void of darkness.

He steps forward, his robes swaying from his broad shoulders. "I have been waiting for you," say his many mouths. Their voices speak eerily, not quite in unison, like many echoes. "A mortal cannot outwit a God," he says, "and it is far easier to lure a mouse into a trap, than to hunt for it in the endless fields. Your luck has come to an end, and your world will soon bow before me!" Your enemy thrusts out his hand, then a streak of black lightening rips from his claw-like fingers and surges towards you.

There is no avoiding this attack. Evoka's magic will hone in on you no matter where you go.

If you are wearing the **Ethereal Armour of the Immortals**, turn to **17**.

If not, turn to **186**.

124

As the army gets nearer to the bend, you come to a giant shard of rock that thrusts up from the middle of the valley floor. The natural formation is more than one hundred feet in height, and if you were to climb to the top you would have a good view over the landscape. This could be a perfect opportunity to see what dangers lurk ahead.

If you have the special ability of **Scale**, or if you possess a pair of **Spiked Climbing Boots**, you may ask Faranen to halt his army while you climb to the top of the structure. If you wish to do this, turn to **165**.

Otherwise, you push on around the bend, turn to **73**.

125

When you reach the cobbled square by the main gate, you are greeted to a scene of utter chaos. People are running this way and that, panicking and yelling. The huge, locked gate is shaking and rattling, as if something is trying to beat it down. A tall, stone wall encircles the town, so you rush up onto the ramparts to see what is happening. A line of archers have already gathered there, raining arrows upon the dreaded army that is assaulting the town. A host of skeletal figures, some clad in ancient armour, surge and swirl at the foot of the main gate, tearing and ripping at the wood with their jagged bone-fingers. They are seemingly immune to the arrows that are showering down on them, and their mindless, puppetlike movements suggest that they are being controlled by a dreaded Necromancer. You scan the army, and you soon spot the silhouette of a tall figure, who is standing at the centre of the chaos; he must be the height of two large men, and he is clad in dark armour from head to toe. His outline seems to move and flicker, as if he is made of an intangible energy that surges with power. You suspect that you have found the master of this rabble, but he is beyond the reach of the archers, so you decide to concentrate your efforts on helping the defenders.

A young man in heavy armour is standing down in the courtyard. He is calling to anyone with a sword to come to his side. "The gate will not hold for long," he is yelling. "I need help."

You can see that the main gate is beginning to crack under the assault, so you decide to run down and join him. As you dash along the walkway towards the stairs, you notice that several Skeletons are climbing the walls. The archers are firing at them, but their arrows are having no effect. "Don't leave us," calls a bowman. "Those things will reach the summit of the wall at any moment! We need you here!"

If you stay to help the archers, turn to **65**.

If you hurry down to the main gate, turn to **130**.

If you hatch a plan to escape the town, turn to **40**.

There was once a clear road through the fields, but it has now become overgrown with long grass. The nearby crops are withering in the autumn chill and the morning sun tints everything with its crimson hue, making it look as if a bloody battle has already taken place here.

When you are about a mile from the city walls, you see an abandoned cottage ahead and to your left. As you draw nearer, a ghostly clattering begins to rise on the breeze, then the men grip their swords with tense expressions. As you pass by the shadowy structure, ten Skeletons shuffle out from the shade of the building. They move towards the soldiers, but the undead horrors are massively outnumbered, and the Amossans quickly obliterate them.

Faranen halts the army. "Let us check the building for more enemies. We should destroy every trace of evil that we find," he says. "There are barns around the back of the building which also need to be investigated. When the area has been made safe, we will push on towards the mountain."

He asks for five volunteers to go with him into the barns.

If you agree to be one of the volunteers, turn to **83**.
If not, turn to **151**.

The huge Skeleton is still gripping one spear, and it has now set its sights on Faranen. The king is seated on his horse several metres to your left, and the Giant starts wading through the crowd towards him.

If you wish to push forward to stop it from reaching the king, turn to **162**.

If you would rather let Faranen deal with the Giant, turn to **208**.

As you progress, the way becomes deathly quiet. The grey clouds thicken, causing you to lose sight of the cave entrance and the men behind you. The air feels cold and dank, and the visibility is now so poor that you can barely see your feet upon the old, rune-etched steps.

Suddenly, to your astonishment, the air grows warmer. The clouds start to fade away, and you are stunned by what is revealed. You halt in amazement. You are no longer standing on the grey steps of the mountain. You have been transported somewhere else, to a lush green field on a high plateau, overlooking a scene of rolling, purple meadows. Large planets with swirling, colourful atmospheres sit in a cloudless sky, and you realise that you are no longer on your home world!

A beautiful lady stands before you, dressed in long white robes. Her hair flows slowly, as if blown by a dreamlike wind, yet there is not a breath of movement in the air.

"Where am I?" you gasp.

The woman answers you. Her voice is gentle and soothing, yet her very breath seems to glitter with unimaginable power. "Your body still stands on the steps of the cold mountain," she says. "But I have summoned your spirit here, so that you may speak with me."

You gaze downwards, and you see that your hands and body have become semi-transparent, ghostly and strange.

The woman's gleaming eyes send a shiver through your soul.

"Do you not recognise me?" she asks. "Was it not you who knelt by my statue? Was it not you who prayed at my shrine, when all others overlooked it?"

"You are the lady Tirasel," you say, with a sudden understanding, "the Goddess of Dreams. I saw your statue in the palace gardens; it was overgrown with weeds."

She nods. "Yet still you stopped and prayed to me," she says. "I have been watching you, mortal, for your deeds have been of interest to me. It was not easy for me to bring you here, and I cannot keep you in this place for long, so listen carefully and heed my words. Evoka is a threat to all good things, even me, and thus I feel compelled to aid you. His power is growing. Like a flame in a field, if he is not stopped, he will soon destroy everything around him." She looks towards a distant waterfall, that pours slowly from the sky, down into a sparkling lake. The wondrous scene is at odds with her expression, which is dark and troubled. "Your quest is in peril," she tells you. "Evoka, The Great Deceiver, has lured you into a trap. He knew that you would seek to destroy the gateway, so he is waiting to ambush you at the final stage of your journey."

At her words, a sense of dread flutters through you, but you steady your courage. "What should I do?" you implore. "I cannot turn back. Evoka must be defeated."

"Indeed," she agrees. "If I had the power to stop him myself, I would do so. But I am a Goddess of peace; he is a machine of war. I can exist only in the Land of Dreams, whilst he is tangible and mighty. He is far more powerful than I, but I am not as helpless as he may like to believe." She places her hand on your shoulder, and you feel a sudden transference of strength pouring into you. "With my blessings, you may have half a chance against him," she says. "Now go, back to your own world, and make swiftly into the cave. Do not waste a moment, for my gifts cannot exist for long outside of the Dream World."

Suddenly, a great wind tears at you, then the image of the Goddess vanishes before your eyes. The waterfall, the fields, the planets, all melt into a kaleidoscope of colour, then a white light overcomes you.

You feel a dank chill in the air, and you suddenly find yourself lying on the steps of the cold mountain, surrounded by grey cloud. Your head feels muggy, as if you have been asleep, and you feel briefly disorientated. As you get to your feet, you begin to feel a strange power rising in your veins. Your sword has vanished, but it has been replaced by a new one. The blade is shimmering with a dream-like luminance and your body is encased in a ghostly glow. (Erase your old weapon and any Damage Bonuses from your Character Sheet, then make a note that you are carrying the **Dream-Sword of Tirasel**. You should also write that you are encased in the **Ethereal Armour of the Immortals**.)

You remember Tirasel's warning – that her gifts and blessings will not last for long in this world – so you decide to make your way swiftly to the top of the steps.

Turn to **77**.

129

As you turn towards the cellar's exit, you spot another hatchway in the floor. It emits a long creak as you pull it open. You see more, narrower steps, leading down into an even deeper, darker cellar.

If you descend to the next level, turn to **260**.

If you leave and return to the ship, turn to **338**.

130

The main gate is still intact, but you suspect that it will not hold for much longer against the fierce onslaught. You quickly join a growing number of men who are gathering there. You see people of all ages, some young, some weathered and old, but all armed with an assortment of weapons. When a good sized crowd has amassed, a young soldier moves to the head of the group and starts to bark orders. Within a minute he has organised the rabble into a defensive formation. Men stand shoulder to shoulder, six rows deep, with spearmen at the back and swordsmen at the front. You stand side to side with the soldier in command. The man's name is Rowfur, and although he is young, his scarred face marks him as an experienced warrior. The gate suddenly shudders violently, then more cracks appear in the wood. The massive hinges squeal and groan, but for the moment they are holding.

Rowfur turns, and you can see that he is about to address the group.

Will you interrupt him and ask if he has any information about the attacking horde, turn to **149**.

Or will you wait to see what he has to say, turn to **50**.

131

"Hold your ground!" you yell. "Not matter what happens, we cannot let the enemy through this gate."

A wild arrow, sprung from the bow of an undead enemy, suddenly sweeps down and thuds into your shoulder. (Reduce your **Life Force** by two points.)

You drag the arrow free and continue fighting. Your refusal to give up galvanises the other men. With grim faces, they rally together and muster the last shreds of their energy. Turn to **55**.

132

Suddenly, up on the rise, the muttering voices halt. A hissing noise makes you turn, and you see that an old, hunched woman has materialised behind you. A moment later, several little hags, with round shoulders, black hair and tattered robes, appear in a circle all around, pointing their wands in your direction.

"Well well," mutters one, in a croaky voice, "Where did *you* come from?"

"Looks like it fell through WrettleNeck's mirror!" says the smallest of the group. "What a treat! Best heat up the cauldron! He looks tasty indeed!"

"He?" snaps a third, "I thought it was a woman!"

"Could be either," replies the first, "all humans are so ugly, it is quite hard to tell. Let us call it a girl, just to avoid confusion. They all taste the same anyway."

The whole coven starts to mutter in agreement, whilst nodding their heads.

"Keep your distance, you old hags," you exclaim, gripping your sword. "I have been sent on a quest by one of your own kind, to defeat the God, Evoka. You must send me back through the mirror, so that I can complete my task."

"Ahhhh," they hiss, exhaling with ghastly breaths. "Then you are the one that the Nameless Witch spoke of!"

They begin chattering and shaking their heads with disapproval and anger. "There'll be no time to complete your quest now," says the shortest figure. "Evoka is on the move, and he has already laid waste to half the land."

"Nonsense!" you snap, "your lies will get you nowhere. Evoka is resting in the Land of the Dead. I must destroy the portal between worlds, before it is too late. Now end this nonsense and send me back from whence I came."

"It is already too late," she exclaims. "You are far indeed from WrettleNeck's house, and you did not travel here in seconds; when you stepped through the gate, many weeks passed in the blink of your eye. Your quest is doomed. Evoka has already returned, and if you step back through the glass, even more weeks will pass, and the world will be very different by the time you re-emerge in WrettleNeck's dwelling. By passing through the mirror, you have doomed yourself, and us all, so we may as well make a meal of you, and enjoy our last nights, before the terrible shadow reaches us."

They move towards you with bloodthirsty expressions, but as they straighten their wands, you suddenly see the reflections changing in the mirror. You cannot defeat the coven: small and feeble they may be, but you will stand no chance against their many, powerful wands. You suddenly spring towards the glass, catching them off guard, and you manage to slice through a Witch as you go. Crackling lightning erupts from several wands at once, but the temperature suddenly changes, the world distorts, then you find yourself back in the dark room at the Fortune Teller's house. Turning, you quickly shatter the glass with your sword, so that nothing can follow you through the mirror. You race up the stairs, your heart beating frantically with dread. You can only hope that the Witches were lying, and that you still have time to complete your quest.

Turn to **349**.

133

As you walk onwards, the moon slowly grows higher above the crooked buildings. Pelanthius moves ahead with purposeful strides, his robes trailing behind him. A blue glow emanates from his staff, lighting the way, and you soon notice a wall with a poster nailed to it. It is a portrait of an ominous looking figure; a murderous man with savage eyes. You pause and glimpse the text beneath the drawing:

Blood-Gor the Pirate, Captain of the Black Ship,
was recently spotted sailing
in the waters around Kattaran.
Two trading vessels have vanished
in the last month.
Let this be a warning to all.

"Come come," says Pelanthius, who has moved ahead, without noticing the poster. "We have no time to spare, my dear friend."

You continue onwards and soon see a side turning. A signpost points towards it which reads: *This way to Desecration Hill.*

If you explore the turning, turn to **266**.

If you walk on, turn to **388**.

With a final, massive sword strike, you manage to obliterate your enemy's skull. The creature stops moving and the glow fades from its shattered mouth.

(If you possess a **Boar-Tusk Bow**, you notice that it has been broken in the fall. Remove it from your Character Sheet.)

A battle-scarred soldier pulls you to your feet and checks that you are okay. You have no time to thank him, as you are quickly separated by the bustling movement of people. You can no longer see your horse, as you are now surrounded by a mix of Amossan warriors and flame-eyed enemies, all locked in a battle for survival. A skeletal figure leaps at you from your right, but you quickly obliterate it with a crushing sword strike. After your last clash, these Skeletons seem like easy pickings, and you quickly hack your way through several opponents. As the battle continues, you notice that the nearby soldiers have been distracted by something in the sky. Glancing up, you see several ghostly phantoms descending towards you from the clouds. A young soldier, who is standing nearby, fires upwards with his Amossan War Bow, but his spinning arrow passes harmlessly through the bodies of the demented apparitions.

(These ghastly beings can only be harmed by powerful spells, so you must think of a plan.)

If you possess a **Black-Wood Wand**, turn to **36**.

If not, turn to **384**.

Your blade suddenly strikes the Demon Stone, shattering it against the king's breastplate. Tiny fragments scatter like black glass across the floor, then a terrible rumble rises up through the vaulted ceiling, as if a dark spell has been vanquished from the room. Faranen pauses in mid strike. The curse has been lifted from him, and he looks suddenly confused, as if he has just woken from a terrible nightmare.

"Why am I holding my sword?" he exclaims. "What is happening here?!"

"You were under the grip of a spell," you tell him. "The curse of a Demon Stone was upon you, but the artefact has been destroyed!"

The king drops his sword and quickly helps the dazed guard to his feet.

You speak to the king and tell him everything that has just occurred. He has no memory of fighting you, nor can he recollect anything from the past week. It is as though he has been trapped in a dream state the whole time, his actions dictated by the power of the stone. "The last thing I remember is receiving the necklace as a gift," he says. "A traveller from the north gave it to me; a kind man in ragged clothes."

You tell him that the traveller was probably a Demon in disguise - an enemy of Amossa - and you explain everything regarding your meeting with the Witch and of your adventures thereafter. You also tell him of the danger that is sweeping the land, about the Demon Gate and the coming of Evoka.

The king's face becomes ashen with dismay. "I should gather my army," he says immediately. "That portal must be destroyed."

You are relieved to hear his response.

"How soon can your army be ready?" you ask.

"Give me until the morning to organize my troops. I will make sure that you are given the finest horse in Amossa, so that you can ride into battle at my side."

He grips your shoulders with an expression of friendship, then he promises to do all that he can to help you succeed in your quest.

Turn to **155**.

136

"Very well," says the guard, after some deliberation. "I will take you to the king, but only you. Your grey bearded friend can wait here." He points towards your scabbard. "No weapons are allowed in the great hall, except those belonging to the king and his guards. You must leave your swords and such here."

You agree to his demand. (Make a note that you have left all of your weapons outside with Pelanthius. If you own **Night-Slayer**, your **damage bonuses** will vanish until the sword is returned to you.)

The guard orders the troops to part, then he leads you up the steps towards the main entrance. "Your story had better be good," he tells you. "Faranen will not be happy with you, nor I, if it is found that you are wasting his time."

Turn to **10**.

137

The arrow thuds into Kazal's bicep, causing the potion to slip from his hand. (Remove **one Arrow** from your belongings.) The bottle shatters at his feet, then he pulls the arrow from his arm with a cry of pain. In desperation, he falls to his knees and licks several droplets of liquid from a broken shard of glass. You quickly reload your bow, but as you take aim, you see that the Wizard's body has started to shine with a terrible power. Kazal waves his arm, and before you can fire your second shot, your bow suddenly transforms into a writhing, hissing snake. The tiny drop of liquid has increased Kazal's powers tenfold!

Roll one dice to see if luck is with you.

If you roll a three or less, turn to **316**.

If you roll a four or above, turn to **153**.

138

Your enemy lets out a sudden, terrible roar, then he collapses and begins to tremble and disintegrate. Magical energy is bleeding from his wounds, creating black pools of glittering shadow in the island's rocky grooves. A moment later, his body completely crumbles into blackened cinders.

(**Tirasel's Armour** suddenly flickers and vanishes, disappearing forever: remove it from your Character Sheet.)

The magic of the Goddess is fading, and although the **Dream-Sword** is still with you, you sense that it will not remain in this world for much longer.

Suddenly, you feel the presence of evil, growing once more in the heart of the cave. Before your very eyes, Evoka's ashes rise up like black petals, and they begin to float around in the air in front of you. As you watch, they merge together to form a dreaded, sinister mass of pitch darkness. A look of horror is etched onto your face, for you realise what is happening.

Evoka - the Savage God - is returning to life! Tirasel's **Dream-Sword** was not powerful enough to destroy him completely, and in a few moments he will rise again, healed of all his wounds. He will soon be ready to face you in combat for a second time! You are not sure if there is anything you can do to stop this phoenix-like revival, but you cannot simply watch in vain. You must act quickly.

If you use the **Dream-Sword** to attack the reforming mass of darkness, turn to **69**.

If you think you are outmatched, you may turn and flee towards the cave's exit, turn to **356**.

He is happy to share his thoughts. "The first two are very pleasant," he says, "but Dragon's Forge is not for the faint hearted. Barbarians love it, but I'd only recommend that one if yer like having yer throat scolded. The Wishing Well Brew and the Rot-Wood Black Sap cost the same: **one Crimson Coin**. The notorious Dragon's Forge ale costs **two**."

If you want to drink, reduce your money now, then turn to the relevant page.

If you order the Wishing Well Brew, turn to **354**.

If you order a Rot-Wood Black Sap, turn to **376**.

If you order a Dragon's Forge ale, turn to **395**.

If you decide not to drink, turn to **87**.

A shining blade swings towards your throat, but you manage to duck the blow whilst simultaneously cleaving through the ribcage of your enemy. As your opponent falls, you suddenly hear Rowfur cry out in alarm. You glance to your right and see a huge Skeleton storming towards him. It is the lumbering remains of a long dead Hill Giant. Its bones are immensely thick, and it is the height of at least three men. Rowfur tries to defend himself, but his sword is torn from his hand by the brutish, undead horror. At the same moment, a red-haired man is knocked to the ground to your left, and he is set upon by several ghastly figures! You can hear him calling out for support.

Both men are in need of aid, but who will you help first?

If you help Rowfur, turn to **160**.

If you help the man to your left, turn to **220**.

Before you can stop him, Kazal throws the liquid into his mouth. His hands suddenly shake and tremble, then his body starts to swell and grow. You have no idea what is about to happen. Due to the unstable chemical ingredients of the potion, even Kazal cannot be exactly sure of the outcome.

Roll one dice to discover the result.

If you roll a three or less, turn to **350**.

If you roll a four or higher, turn to **320**.

142

A cold gust of night wind blows down the narrow pass, creaking the signs as you walk onwards. You soon reach a small shop run by a little old lady with a friendly face. Looking through the door, you see a collection of small, wood carved animals. The creative ornaments fill the interior, but they are for decorative purposes only, and are of no use to you.

As you turn to leave, the old woman speaks, inviting you to enter.

If you step inside, turn to **223**.

If you continue down the lane, turn to **373**.

143
Illustration Opposite & Overleaf

As you enter the cramped hut, the first thing you notice is the burning fireplace. A large, bubbling pot hangs above the flames, and a strange aroma fills the air. The dancing firelight illuminates the cobwebs that crisscross the ceiling, and you see a fat toad watching you from a nearby bookshelf.

The Witch shuffles towards a round table and perches on the edge of a chair. "For several years," she says, "you have been a thorn in the side of many evil things. Countless wicked creatures have been slain by your sword, with many a foul plan undone. But when you slew the Demon King earlier this year, his three closest relatives – Ganthor, Korovar and Golgorast – swore to get revenge. The trio called to the Spirit Winds, and they sent a message into the Land of the Dead.

They promised to free Evoka from the Underworld, but only if he agreed to tear your body limb from limb. The Spirit Winds called back to them, and the pact was sealed." The Witch waves her hand, and a strange vision briefly appears in the air. You see a dark, jagged mountain, smothered in grey cloud, with flashes of lightening erupting near the summit. "The demonic trio left Cair Nurath and journeyed north," she says. "They went to Amossa, to the peak of Illomen, where the World's Spirit flows wild and strong. There they began a terrible ritual. Sacrifices were made, dark blood ran upon the jagged spires of rock, then they chanted spells that even a Witch would dare not utter. The land grew dark and the mountain shivered. I would have raced into the north to stop them, but alas, I had not expected them to succeed in their plan. It was a grave mistake on my part, for they tore open a doorway between the Land of the Living and The Dead, allowing Evoka to rise up through the breach. For the first time in a thousand years, the King of the Dead set his eyes upon the stars once more." The image of the mountain fades away, then the Witch leans forward, her wrinkled face staring at you through strands of straggly hair. "Evoka must slay you, for the Gods cannot go back on their promises. But once you are dead, he will set his sights upon the rest of the world, and no Witch, Wizard or human will be safe from him. He will reduce this world to dust, draining the life from it to increase his power, for he cannot resist the lure of his destructive nature. He is the King of the Dead, the God of war and chaos.

So, you see, I have no choice but to help you, for this problem affects us all."

The Witch pauses, as if awaiting your response.

What will you say to her?

"How did you learn this information?" Turn to **226**.

"You said that the other Gods banished Evoka into the Underworld. Can we not call on their aid?" Turn to **52**.

144

Before you can act, Rowfur leaps forward. He charges towards the steed and ducks low, swinging his blade in a mighty arc at the horse's front leg. White splinters fly everywhere as he shatters the thick bone. The steed instantly crashes to the ground, throwing the rider from the saddle. Sword in hand, you spring forward to help your brave comrade, and you crush the horseman's skull before it can clamber to its feet. A cheer goes up from the men behind you, then more Skeletons shuffle in through the gap. These ones are all on foot, but they are coming through in heavy numbers, and several men fall in the ensuing chaos. The defensive line is beginning to weaken, and Rowfur looks to you for advice. "I am a man of courage," he says, "but we cannot hold them back forever, the army is too vast. What should we do?"

Will you:

Tell him to fight on, turn to **131**.

Or advise him that the men should abandon the defence and head for the refuge of the town's central keep, turn to **365**.

145

As you surge along the new trail, the mist grows dangerously close. A terrible mouth opens up in the miasma. As it inhales, you feel your energy evaporating, then a searing pain rips through your body. You glance back and see that your enemy is sucking the life out of everything around it. The nearby trees wither and die, then their branches crumble into ash. Sweat pours from your forehead and you feel suddenly breathless and weak. You cling desperately to the reigns, trying not to fall from the steed.

(Reduce your **Life Force** by six points!)

If you are still alive, turn to **8**.

146

Someone suddenly jumps onto your back, causing you to stagger forward, deeper into the fray. You throw him over your shoulder, sending him crashing to the floorboards, then you spin around and see a tabletop flying through the air towards you. You suddenly find yourself wondering why you entered this place! You are struck in the face by the lump of wood, then you topple backwards from the impact. (Reduce your **Life Force** by one point.) You have crashed into a drunken sailor, and he turns towards you and throws a punch at your head.

If you dodge the blow and try to escape from the tavern, turn to **276**.

If you block the attack and fight back, turn to **206**.

147

The giant tentacle falls away into the sea, its blood burning the deck as it slides over the edge. But more slithering arms are rising out of the water, countless in number, and the roar of the monster suggests that your attacks have only increased its anger.

Suddenly, Pelanthius emerges from the hatchway behind you, looking somewhat ruffled. "Forgive my lateness," he calls, "we Wizards are deep sleepers!"

A beam of light instantly leaps from his staff and soars past the bow of the ship. It then arches downwards and strikes the head of the sea beast, which can just be seen amongst the crashing waves. The monster falls silent and ceases its attack. The Wizard's magic has not wounded it; instead, the spell has put it to sleep. The mega beast drifts down into the depths of the sea, its tentacles slithering beneath the surface, then the WindRunner surges loose from the deadly embrace.

Valantis staggers towards the Wizard. "Well done, Grey Beard," he says, "but make your presence known quicker next time!"

You begin to help the wounded, but it is not long before a flustered crewman appears through the hatchway, claiming that the ship is taking on water. With a worried look, you follow Valantis below deck to assess the extent of the damage.

Roll one dice to see if luck is on your side.

If you roll a six, turn to **368**.

If you roll any other number, turn to **167**.

148

You resolve yourself to spending the night in the hut. If you want to explore the Witch's living room, you may:

Take a closer look at the bookshelf, turn to **5**.

Investigate the wooden chest in the corner of the room, turn to **56**.

Examine the small statue that sits above the fireplace, turn to **213**.

Or eat some of the Witch's stew, turn to **161**.

When you are ready, you can get some sleep by turning to **42**.

149

You introduce yourself to Rowfur, who shakes your hand.

"I can see by your stance that you know how to use a weapon," he says. "Thank you for joining the defence, we will need all the numbers we can muster if we are going to hold off these aggressors."

You ask Rowfur why the army is attacking Mosal, but he looks unsure. "I was told that a tall figure arrived outside the gate this morning. It is he who is commanding the army, but I don't know why he has attacked the town. He must be a powerful Necromancer indeed, to raise an army of the dead."

The men to your left overhear Rowfur's comments, and they begin to mutter nervously with expressions of dread. "Some say he is not a Necromancer at all," says the man behind you. "He is not made of flesh and blood, only dark, crackling energy."

"Do not speak such nonsense," snaps Rowfur. "Only the God, Evoka, matches that description, and he has not walked this world for an ageless time."

You are about to ask him more, but the gate is suddenly struck by a massive force. The wood bows inwards, groaning from the impact, and only by the scantest margin does it remain intact. Turn to **50**.

150

Out on the battlefield, the dark figure suddenly raises his fist to the sky, then his deep voice rumbles towards you like the sound of thunder. To your horror, the foul warlord speaks your name! "I have come for you, Demon's Bane," he says. "If you wish for me to spare this town, you must come forth to face me."

You have no idea what this demented figure wants from you, but it is clear that he will rip the town apart in order to get it! He suddenly places his hands upon the ground, as if drawing energy from the earth, and you have a feeling that he is powering up for a devastating attack.

You must do something fast if you are going to save the inhabitants of Mosal.

Do you possess **Sixth Sense**?

If so, turn to **327**.

If not, turn to **180**.

In light of the recent attack, Faranen and his men double-check the buildings, but no further enemies are found. The king returns to the waiting army and gives the order to march on.

Before long, you come to a clifftop path that overlooks the glittering sea. Your trail takes you past two abandoned villages, which have recently been burnt to the ground. As you pass the wreckage, you suddenly notice the long grass – which is almost the height of a man - rustling near the edges of the ruins.

A few minutes ago, did you help Faranen to search the cottage and barns?

If you did, turn to **64**.

If you did not, turn to **173**.

152

The children suddenly stop playing and look towards you. "I wouldn't go into the woods if I were you," says the smallest one. "That path leads up to Kazal's tower. He went mad some time ago, after one of his experiments went wrong."

"What experiment?" you ask, with a worried expression.

The boy shrugs. "I don't know all the details, but I heard he went mad after drinking one of his potions. Overnight, it turned him from a good man into a paranoid maniac. I guess that's the risk you take when you mess around with magic!"

"That's not what happened," snaps his friend. "He cast a spell which went wrong, and he accidentally turned himself into a wild beast."

"Rubbish!" says the other, rather angrily. "I'm not wrong! You don't know what you're talking about!"

They start to argue over who is right, then their disagreement descends into a childish scuffle.

You grab them by the collars and pull them apart. "Calm yourselves," you demand. "This is no time for foolishness." You ask them if they saw a Wizard named Pelanthius, recently passing this way, and you describe his sweeping beard and pointed hat.

"I don't know," answers one of them in a moody tone, whilst staring irritably at his friend. "We only just got here." They pull away from you and run off in the direction of the town, chasing each other in circles and calling each other childish names. You decide you had better set off towards the tower straight away, to see if there is any truth in either boy's story. You quickly race up the wooded trail. Turn to **57**.

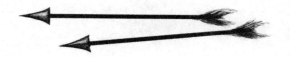

You hurl the snake to the floor, then dodge to the left as a ball of crackling energy soars from the Wizard's hand. There is a huge boom and the blast completely destroys the wall behind you. A massive crack appears across the stone ceiling, then you hear the building groan and creak. Fearing that the roof is about to collapse, you grab Pelanthius and drag him towards the exit.

"Fool," mutters Kazal. "You cannot escape me!"

In the hysteria of his madness, he has not noticed the expanding crack in the ceiling. He starts to descend the stairs, whilst muttering the words to another spell. You haul Pelanthius out through the front door, then the vaulted roof suddenly collapses.

A huge block of masonry crashes into Kazal, slamming him to the ground, then he is buried under a mass of debris. Turn to **163**.

You quickly swerve in the saddle, hoping to avoid the plunging spears. Two narrowly miss you, the other gouges your side. Reduce your **Life Force** by three points.

If you are still alive, turn to **127**.

Faranen invites you to spend the night in the palace, and he extends the same courtesy to Pelanthius. You are both shown to separate bedrooms, whose balconies overlook the rooftops of the moon drenched city.

(If you were forced to leave your weapons outside, they have now been returned, and you have discarded the shortsword.) Fine food is brought to you, along with a goblet of Amossan wine, and you feast well in the privacy of your quarters. (Increase your **Life Force** by three points.) As you are finishing your meal, there comes a knock at your door, and you see a palace guard standing there with a bottle of glittering, red liquid. "A gift from the king," he says, holding it out to you. As you take it, he turns and disappears down the corridor.

You study the label and realise that you are holding a very rare and magical potion. (You may drink it at any time, even during close combat, and it will instantly increase your **Life Force** by ten points! You can either drink it now, or you may add it to your inventory for use at a later date. If you decide to keep it, note it down under the title **Potion of the Phoenix**, along with its effects.)

You are now feeling very sleepy, but you know that a great battle awaits in a few hours.

Your head is bustling with thoughts, so you decide to calm your mind with a walk in the palace grounds. You make your way through the white halls to the sanctum of the inner gardens. The tree-lined ponds sparkle in the moonlight, and it is clear that the grounds are generally well kept. However, in a forgotten corner, where weeds have grown long and thick, you come to a lonely building that is covered in ivy. It looks far older than the rest of the palace, as though the city might have grown up around it. Six white pillars - each ten feet in height - hold up a cracked roof, and the elegant statue of a beautiful woman stands beneath it. It is the effigy of Tirasel, The Goddess of Dreams. Legend once said that she was the enemy of Evoka, but she has been forgotten here. Her ancient shrine looks sad and worn, left to fade in the corner of the garden. After dragging the vines from her slender shoulders, you sit and pray, asking her to bless you with luck in the battle ahead. When you are done, you head back to your room and lay down. You pull a heap of fur covers around you and drift into a peaceful sleep. Your mind is calm and tranquil, and you rest quietly until the dawn.

Turn to **193**.

Valantis leads you to a large room at the stern of the ship. Coastal charts, a sextant, and other sailing instruments are dotted around the space. Moonlight shines in through the surrounding windows, and you can see the dark sea shimmering in the silvery light. Valantis lights two lanterns and sits opposite you. He explains that the game you will be playing is called Ships and Serpents. He gives you a dice and keeps one for himself. You notice that the dice have pictures on all six sides.

"One of us must play as a Pirate, the other as a Merchant," Valantis tells you. "As you are probably new to this game, I'll let you choose which one you want to be."

(Read the following instructions so that you know how to play the game, then make your choice as to who will play as the Pirate and who will be the Merchant. You can only change your mind at the start of each new round. If you are shrewd and lucky, this may be an opportunity to increase your money. To play one round of the game, roll two dice. Add them together to get your **Score**. Once you have done this, look at the chart on the following page. Valantis will quit the match immediately after the fifteenth round, so you had best keep track of how many rounds you play. You can end the game sooner if you wish.)

Score	Result	Winner/Loser
2	There is a picture of a Sea Beast facing upwards on one of the dice	Both you and Valantis lose. You must both hurl one coin each into the sea.
3-8	There is a picture of a merchant ship facing upwards on one dice, and a harbour on the other	Whoever is playing as a Merchant wins two coins from the other player
9-12	There is a picture of a Pirate ship facing upwards on one dice and a merchant vessel on the other	Whoever is playing as a Pirate wins three coins from the other player

When one of you decides to end the game (or if you run out of money), turn to **174**.

At your request, the soldier gives you directions to the palace, then you set off into the city. The area is vast and sprawling, but fortunately the lanes are well signposted. Glowing lanterns hang from tall iron posts, casting their yellow light across the night-blue streets. After a short while, you pass the entrance to a winding alley called Merchant's Way. Despite the late hour, you see several shops down the side turning with their doors hanging open.

If you want to take a detour to see what goods are for sale, turn to **172**.

If you want to ignore the side turning and press on towards the palace, turn to **103**.

158

Suddenly, several of the soldiers halt and grip their heads. One by one they fall to their knees, stricken with agony.

You realise that a dark spell has been cast over the steps, to stop anyone from reaching the cave's entrance.

If Pelanthius is travelling with you, turn to **113**.

If you told Pelanthius to remain in the valley below, to help the wounded, turn to **176**.

The little shop is cramped and dusty. The walls are crammed with shelves, which in turn are crammed with corked bottles. There is a small counter at the back where the scrawny old owner – presumably Rejanji - peers at you from behind his large spectacles. "Prices are on the labels," he says, in a rather ill-tempered manner. "Take a look around, but don't think about stealing anything! I have a wand under my desk and I know how to use it." You assure him that you are a person of honour, but he merely huffs and watches you suspiciously. You spend a good while scanning the shelves. Most of the potions have esoteric names, but three items do catch your attention. If you want to buy anything from the list below, you may purchase them now; adjust your money accordingly.

(Note: because they are so small, you may drink the **Health Potions** at any time, even during combat. Their effects are instantaneous. When you use a potion, remove it from your Character Sheet.)

A **Tiny Health Potion** that will add two points
to your **Life Force** (Two available)
Cost: **one Crimson Coin** each

A **Small Health Potion** that will add five points
to your **Life Force** (One available)
Cost: **three Crimson Coins**

When you are ready to leave, turn to **325**.

160

You surge forward to defend your comrade.

(When you have reduced your opponent's **Life Force** to 5 or below, turn immediately to **25**.)

SKELETAL GIANT

LIFE FORCE   16   STRIKING SPEED   7

Focus	Move	Damage
1	**Tearing Fangs**	2
2-3	**Claws of Bone**	2
4-5	**Sweeping Blade**	3
6	**Mighty Sword Strike**	4

161

You take the pot off of the fire and put it onto the table. Once the brew has cooled, you scoop it into the ladle and take your first sip. You are immediately struck by the horrendous taste, yet you feel compelled to keep eating. Two mouthfuls later, you start to feel your wounds healing. The magical brew is having a miraculous effect, so you quickly finish the lot. By the time that the pot is empty, you are feeling vastly better.

(Increase your **Life Force** by ten points!)

Now return to page **148** and pick an option that you have not yet chosen.

162
Illustration Opposite

Your steed stomps the ground with bold ferocity as it turns to face the monster. Several soldiers rush forward to help you, but they are quickly knocked backwards by the undead Giant. You will have to deal with this enemy on your own, and it will not be easy to defeat! Tendrils of black energy are drifting like smoke from the beast's spine, and its chest is shielded by a tarnished breastplate. Its massive skull has not two, but four shadowy eye sockets, and its fanged mouth is a pit of flames. There is no telling what this horned creature would have looked like in life, before the muscles and flesh had withered from its bones, but it must have been a terrifying sight indeed.

(The beast you are facing is an ancient monstrosity. Its race became extinct during the great cataclysm of fire that ravaged the land during the War of the Gods, but now it has returned to cause chaos once more.)

(Special Ability: Because of its many arms and brutal fighting style, your enemy will roll for two moves instead of one; i.e. if it hits you, it will strike you twice simultaneously before you have a chance to retaliate.)

THE ANCIENT ONE

LIFE FORCE 20   STRIKING SPEED 8

Focus	Move	Damage
1	Swiping Claws	2
2-3	Ripping Claws	3
4-5	Jagged Elbow Slam	3
6	Impaling Strike	4

If you defeat this powerful horror, turn to **181**.

163

When the dust has settled, you cautiously head back into the building. As you clamber over the rubble, you see the Wizard lying silently amongst the disorder and chaos. His hair is soaked in blood, and his legs are trapped beneath the heavy slab that felled him. Your bow has returned to normal, and you see it resting nearby on a heap of wreckage. As you pick it up, Kazal suddenly twitches! He is returning to consciousness, so you instantly raise your sword.

"Please," he mutters feebly, "I am too wounded to defend myself. Spare me... Let me speak. I will tell you anything that you want to know."

If you ask him how to defeat Evoka, turn to **184**.

If you strike him whilst you have the chance, turn to **4**.

You spring at the Wizard with your sword raised. In a panic, Kazal raises his staff, but before he can cast another spell, you bring your sword crashing down on his magical weapon. His staff shatters under the impact, then you swing your fist and knock him backwards with a mighty punch. The Wizard crumples to the floor and rolls several feet before halting at the foot of the staircase.

"Give up, Wizard," you tell him. "Your staff is broken and the source of your power is gone."

Kazal's eyes gleam with fury. He suddenly grabs a potion from beneath his robes and hurls it at your feet. The glass explodes against the stone, then a black mist instantly pours out, obscuring your vision. You stab around blindly in the murk, but when the fog clears you see that your devious opponent has fled onto the balcony at the top of the steps. He glares down at you with a furious expression.

"You may have broken my staff," he hisses. "But I am not finished yet. You will not slay me that easily!" He reaches into his pocket, pulls out another potion, then opens his mouth. He is about to drink the contents of the bottle. If you want to stop him, you will have to act quickly.

If you have a **Bow** and want to use it, turn to **13**.

If you do not have a **Bow**, or if you choose not to use it, turn to **141**.

You clamber to the top of the formation. You are at a dizzying height and you can see into the winding pass that lies ahead. What you discover sends a chill through your veins. A skeletal army is stalking down the valley towards the bend in the gorge, and more enemies are moving towards the canyon from both the left and the right. Faranen's army is about to be ambushed from multiple sides! Before you can shout a warning, several ghastly spirits descend from the sky towards you. Their freezing, ghostly hands grab your body and drag you away from the rock face! Your enemies hurl you into open air, and you are sent plunging towards your doom!

Down in the valley, Pelanthius leaps from his steed and shouts the words to an ancient spell. A blast of energy soars upwards from his staff, encasing you in a glowing sphere of light.

Roll one dice to see if luck is with you. If you are wearing an **Enchanted, Emerald Bracelet** or a **Glittering Bone Charm,** add three to the number rolled.

If the total is one or two, the Wizard's spell does not have time to take full effect. It slows your descent, but you are still travelling at a tremendous pace when you hit the ground. Your **Amossan Shield** absorbs the brunt of the impact and it is smashed apart by the sharp rocks. It spares your head and arms from a grisly fate, but your right leg is almost broken against the unforgiving terrain. Reduce your **Life Force** by five points and remove the **Amossan Shield** from your inventory.

If the total is three to five, the Wizard's spell slows your decent, and it partially cushions your impact as you hit the ground. Although the sphere does not completely spare you from harm, it massively decreases the damage of your landing. Reduce your **Life Force** by two points.

If the total is more than five, the Wizard's spell is cast just in the nick of time. The sphere of light slows your descent and you land gently on the valley floor, none the worse for your ordeal.

If you are still alive, turn to **232**.

166

You tell the barman that you still intend to pay a visit to the old Wizard, as it is important that you speak to him.

He shakes his head, as if convinced that you are unwise. "If I cannot dissuade you, I should at least warn you about the track that leads up to his home. In his madness, Kazal poisoned the stream that winds through the woods, effecting the trees that drink from it. Come night time, the trees come to life and attack anyone who comes near them. Be on your guard if you take the path through the woods."

You thank him for his information, then you leave the building. You decide to go in search of Pelanthius, to warn him of what you have learnt.

Turn to **198**.

167

The ship is indeed taking on water, but Pelanthius manages to slow the leak with a powerful spell. He casts a magical shield around the fracture in the boat, but he is unable to fix the problem completely.

"The WindRunner's hull has been cracked by the enemy," says the captain, "and I fear that she is beyond repair." His face is lined with misery, and you can hear the woe in his voice.

Pelanthius acknowledges that he will not be able to keep the WindRunner afloat for long.

"Keep us intact if you can," says Valantis. "If we sink this far from land, we'll be in serious trouble!"

For the next few hours, as the bad news spreads, the sailors become silent and tense. The storm fades, but a brisk wind continues to push the WindRunner through the choppy waters. By the time that dawn breaks, the crack in the hull has widened. Pelanthius is struggling to keep the sea at bay, and crewmen begin to bail water from the hold. Come dusk, the vessel starts to groan, as if preparing to give itself up to the sea.

"This ship is coming apart," says Pelanthius, with an exhausted voice. "I can no longer hold her together."

The captain nods and orders everyone to abandon the vessel. From the refuge of several longboats, you watch as the WindRunner groans and lists to the side. Under the rising moon, the once fine vessel sinks beneath the dark waters, where it vanishes forever. There is a stillness amongst the crew. The sad eyed captain orders the men to row onwards, and they do so in grim silence.

A short while later, in the frosty darkness, you see the lights of Port Acura. You slowly move towards them.

Turn to **118**.

168

The underground corridors would be pitch-black were it not for the Wizard's glowing staff. As you wander through the passages, you notice cryptic little symbols, etched on the walls. They look meaningless, but Kazal must have put them there for a reason. You eventually realise what you are looking at. They are encrypted directions, telling you to head north, then east, then west. Curious, you follow the signs. Turn to **96**.

169

Ugluk is appalled by your move, as are the spectators.

"Get that coward out of here," shouts a man to your left. The crowd lift you up and carry you to the exit, then you are thrown into the street.

The door is slammed shut behind you.

You get to your feet and stagger away from the building. Turn to **198**.

You suddenly hear the bending and snapping of timbers, and a large crack appears in the hull. Before you can escape, water gushes in, knocking you off of your feet. For a brief moment you are surrounded by swirling bubbles. You spin around in the chaos and slam your head against the side of the ship. (Reduce your **Life Force** by two points.) If you are alive, you burst above the surface and drag yourself out of the hold. You are now on the second level, but the ship is leaning further and further to starboard. You shake yourself to your senses and sprint towards the hatchway that leads onto the top deck. Turn to **380**.

"The captain is busy," they tell you. "As are we." They return to their work, lugging the heavy boxes up the gangplank. You need to regain their attention, so you step forward and help with the crates. The workers are surprised and grateful for your aid, and it takes over an hour before the ship is fully loaded. The men pat you on the back and thank you for your help, then one of them hands you his hip flask. "Have a drink," he says, "it'll put some fire back in yer veins."

Loading the vessel was thirsty work, so you take a large swig before handing it back to him.

(The harsh brew makes your eyes water, but the alcohol has been mixed with droplets from a healing potion, and it revives your energy. Increase your **Life Force** by two points.)

"So," says the sailor, "you wanted to speak to the captain, didn't you?"

You nod and tell him that you are looking for a ship to take you to Port Acura.

"Well, I'm sure I can help you," he says. "Go to the West Wind Tavern and ask for a man named Valantis. He'll give ya a bunk on The WindRunner, though he'll charge you a fee." He gives you directions and bids you farewell.

You thank him, then you set off with Pelanthius. You soon find yourself outside the tavern, which is tucked away in a dark turning called *Hangover Lane*. Laughter and rowdy conversation greets your ears as you step in through the door. Turn to **233.**

Tall buildings lean over you as you proceed down the winding back lane. Pelanthius halts by the first door, his moustache twitching with interest. A sign above the entrance reads *Mortarf's Scrolls*.

You follow the Wizard into the narrow and dusty shop. A handful of glowing candles float magically in the air above you, casting deep shadows between the rows of books. You are uninterested in the spell scrolls – they are of no use to a warrior - so you wait while Pelanthius thumbs through the paperwork. The shop owner is sitting behind his desk at the back of the room, his crooked nose poking from the darkness beneath his hat. He is reading a book and seems uninterested in your presence.

If you ask him about King Faranen and the troubles that have beset Amossa, turn to **202**.

If you remain quiet until Pelanthius is done, turn to **53**.

173

A trio of stealthy killers are creeping through the grass towards Faranen's army. They are Hounds of the Underworld, sent by Evoka to stalk the fields around the mountain! Suddenly, all three of them leap out of the grass towards Pelanthius. The creatures look like misshapen dogs, with rib bones sticking out through their maggot infested fur. Their eyes are cavernous sockets of fire, and their lipless mouths reveal long, yellow fangs. In a flash, a freezing white beam leaps from Pelanthius's staff, striking one of the beasts. The creature shatters like ice in mid-air, but the other two manage to pull the Wizard from his steed. You leap from your horse, as does Faranen, and you both rush to his aid. (You fight one horror, whilst Faranen deals with the second. The Hounds are sprightly and savage, proving hard to hit!)

HOUND OF THE UNDERWORLD

LIFE FORCE 8   STRIKING SPEED   10

Focus	Move	Damage
1	Ferocious Ram	1
2-3	Slashing Claws	2
4-5	Chomping Fangs	2
6	Mauling Frenzy	3

If you win, you turn around and see that Faranen and his men have defeated the second beast. You pull the grateful Wizard to his feet, then you help him back into the saddle. During the skirmish, Pelanthius's staff was knocked from his hand, but you quickly seek it out and return it to him. Turn to **64**.

174

You bid Valantis goodnight, then you go to find your bunk. As you are walking through a quiet part of the ship, you hear the creak of a floorboard behind you.

Do you possess **Sixth Sense**?

If so, turn to **324**.

If not, turn to **187**.

You stagger out of the chair and hurry to the edge of the tower. You gaze down upon your enemy's smashed remains, which are scattered all over the town.

Clayton leaps to your side, roaring with triumph. "Well done my friend! That has bought us some time, but we must still find a way of halting this army." He looks around and his eyes fall upon the tall figure at the centre of the attacking horde. "There is our enemy!" he growls. "Look how magic streams from his hands, giving life to the Skeletons around him. He is controlling this evil horde. If we can find a way to stop him, his army might fall apart and become a useless pile of bones once more."

Clayton may be right, but there is no way to reach the ominous figure.

"It is a shame that we had only one arrow in the Dragon slaying machine," he mutters.

As you are considering your options, the main gate suddenly collapses under the weight of the onslaught. The horde surges forward, but a hardy group of warriors have now gathered by the entrance. A great battle erupts as the men try to stop the enemy from flowing through the breach.

With Clayton at your side, you rush down to help the defenders.

For five minutes a bloody skirmish rages. People fall around you, and you lose sight of Clayton in the chaos.

Turn to **55**.

176

For reasons that you do not understand, you alone are immune to the dark magic that is protecting the cave entrance. You tell the men to move backwards. They crawl down the steps, their pain fading as they do so. They cannot follow you up the ancient path, so you tell them to wait for your return. Their eyes are filled with worry as you turn and ascend the steps.

Turn to **128**.

177

To your horror, you see a huge slab of stone falling towards a young child. You rush towards her, pushing several people out of the way, then you grab her wrist and yank her into your arms. There is a great boom as the slab smashes into the ground where the girl was just standing. The Dragon vanishes from sight, but you suspect that it will return soon. The girl is crying inconsolably, but a worried woman appears from the crowd and takes her from your arms. You notice a resemblance between them, and you guess that the woman is her mother. The lady starts to shower you with thanks, but the surging crowd sweeps her up and you are parted by the flow of people. For a few moments you are caught in the whirlpool of disorder. You see women and children being pushed around and several elderly people are knocked to the ground. As you help them to their feet, the throng begins to disperse. Through the thinning crowd, you suddenly spot the entrance to the sewers. Turn to **292**.

The alley soon opens into a circular, stone walled garden, in the middle of which sits a quaint little cottage. You are surprised by the abundance of butterflies, and there is a strong presence of magic here; you can see it glittering amongst the flowerbeds and sparkling in the thatched roof.

As you walk up to the entrance, you see that a letter has been pinned to the door. 'Forgive my absence,' it reads, 'but I have been called away on urgent matters, and I may be gone for several days. Feel free to rest in my garden during the daylight hours. I shall return as soon as circumstances allow.' You sigh with disappointment, for you sense an aura of goodness in this place, and you would have been intrigued to have met the owner.

If you follow the advice on the note, and sit for a while in the garden, turn to **343**.

If you have the special ability of **Picklock**, and wish to open the door, turn to **304**.

If you walk back down the alley, turn to **198**.

"It's not for sale," he says.

You try to convince him to make a trade, but he becomes irritated by your persistence. He picks up the lantern and locks it in a cupboard beneath his desk. The shopkeeper's rudeness is beginning to wear on your patience, so you decide to leave the building.

Turn to **53**.

180

If you tell your enemy to withdraw his army, so that you can face him in combat, one against one, turn to **22**.

To think of a different plan, turn to **382**.

181

Your mighty adversary topples forward and crashes into the sea of battling opponents. A wild cheer rises up at your victory, but your troubles are not over yet!

A skeletal hand suddenly grabs your leg. As you look down, you are overcome with an expression of horror. The four armed monstrosity is still moving, and despite now having a wrecked body and two smashed legs, it manages to drag you off of your horse. You crash onto the rocks alongside it, then it pulls itself on top of you, entangling you in its twisted mass of half shattered ribs.

Are you wielding the black sword, **Night-Slayer**?

If you are, turn to **134**.

If not, turn to **318**.

182
Illustration Opposite

You scramble onto the deck to get a better view of the scene. You now know what happened to the crew of the abandoned vessel, as their severed limbs are hanging like trophies from the sides of the enemy ship.

The pirates ram into The Sea Star, and the sudden jolt knocks you from your feet. You hit your head on the hard, slippery deck and the blow momentarily dazes you.

As you shake yourself to your senses, you see that the enemy has started to board your vessel, and a battle instantly erupts between the Pirates and the merchant sailors. Glancing to your left, you see a tall, fearsome individual rushing across the deck towards you. He has a snarling mouth of rotten teeth, a wild beard, and a collection of human bones which hang from his belt. You realise that you are facing the evil captain of the enemy ship, and just by his psychotic expression, it is clear that he is a merciless killer.

If you have a **Bow** and any remaining arrows, you may fire at your enemy before he reaches you. If you want to do this, turn to **259**.

If you do not have a bow, or if you would rather defend yourself with your sword, turn to **284**.

183

A line of Skeletons suddenly appear over the valley's ridge to your left. As the Amossans turn towards them, more enemies emerge from around the bend ahead.

"An ambush," snarls Faranen. "Lock shields. Ready your swords!"

Ancient Skeletons in tattered armour, many with tarnished weapons of old, bear down on the Amossans. There are nine hundred warriors in Faranen's army and over three thousand undead horrors! These are the guardians of the mountain pass, whose sole purpose is to stop anyone from reaching the dark gateway!

The first wave of Skeletons crash into the Amossan lines, hammering their swords against the wall of shields. The men heave and hold their footing, then they retaliate by hacking into the sea of horrors. Sitting aloft your mighty steed, you have a good view of the whole battlefield. You are just behind the front line, and you can see that the men are struggling to hold back the surging throng of evil figures. Suddenly, a group of enemies break through the Amossan shield-wall and attempt to drag you from your steed. You refuse to be unseated, and in a show of defiance, you hack down with your mighty blade.

(You should immediately reduce the trio's **Life Force** by eight points, as they are also taking a battering from the Amossan soldiers who are gathered around you.)

TRIO OF SKELETONS

LIFE FORCE	21	STRIKING SPEED	8

Focus	Move	Damage
1	**Ripping Bone Claws**	1
2-3	**Emerald Blade Strike**	2
4-5	**Thrusting Spear**	2
6	**Hacking Scimitar**	3

If you win, turn to **119**.

"Very well," he says weakly. "I will give you the knowledge that you desire." You pause in anticipation, but instead of answering you, a toxic web suddenly erupts from the palm of his hand.

You dodge backwards, narrowly avoiding the attack, then you hear Kazal laughing insanely. Huge legs suddenly sprout from every part of his body, while thick black hair consumes his features. The concoction that he tasted earlier is transforming his body and healing his wounds!

"Fool!" he shrieks. "You will never learn my secrets... NEVER!"

Seeing that you have been deceived, you leap forward to strike your enemy, but he has already morphed into a new, terrifying form!

MONSTROUS SPIDER

LIFE FORCE 8   STRIKING SPEED 9

Focus	Move	Damage
1	Speeding Ram	1
2-3	Thrashing, Pounding Legs	1
4-5	Stabbing Fangs	2
6	Spitting Acid	3

If you win, turn to **4**.

You continue walking. Pushing past the bustling people, you soon come across a stall that is selling adventuring equipment. You see a pair of **Spiked Climbing Boots** which are priced at **three Crimson Coins**, and a dark **Fur Coat** priced at **four Crimson Coins**. If you want to buy either of these items, adjust your money accordingly and enter the purchases onto your Character Sheet. When you are ready to continue down the street, turn to **76**.

186

The black tendril of lightning slams into you with the force of a thousand sword strikes. You are not just slain, your body is obliterated from existence - eradicated from the face of the cosmos - so that not even your dust will be left to litter the world.

Turn to **390**.

You are suddenly struck across the back of the head, and you stagger forward from the impact!

(Reduce your **Life Force** by two points!)

If you are still alive, you whirl around and see two crewmen, one wearing brutish knuckle-dusters, the other carrying a club. "Give us ya money," the taller man snarls. "Or we're gonna beat ya into a pulp."

You refuse to cower, so you draw your sword in a flash of defiance. The shorter man suddenly swings his fist towards your head, but you dodge the blow and slam your sword pommel into his jaw. Several of his teeth are smashed from his mouth, then he crumples to the floorboards in an unconscious state. As he hits the ground, the man with the club surges forward, trying to crack your skull with his weapon. Despite his heavy build, his attacks are fast, and you realise that he is a fighter of considerable skill. You have no choice but to defend yourself.

STOCKY THUG

LIFE FORCE 8   STRIKING SPEED 9

Focus	Move	Damage
1	**Brutish Head-Butt**	1
2-3	**Club to the Ribs**	1
4-5	**Club to the Face**	2
6	**Club to the Skull**	2

If you win, turn to **199**.

188

You step through into a dimly lit, smoky room, filled with the aromas of burning incense. The walls are covered in tapestries which depict the night sky, and a fat spider watches you from its web near the wall-mounted candle.

A thin old woman sits at a round table in the middle of the room, dressed in red robes. Her long grey hair hangs over her shoulders, and her skin is etched with deep wrinkles. By the fineness of her bones, you can tell that she might once have been pretty beyond comparison, but the ravages of time stole her beauty long ago.

She beckons for you to sit in the chair opposite her.

If you do as she asks, turn to **112**.

If you decide to leave, turn to **264**.

189

The books have various titles. They include:

The Uplifting Tale of the Plague,
by Mias WinterMoon

Murder, and Other Fun Hobbies,
by Hegrit BlackThorn

Cooking with Children,
by Haggadus RotWorm

Healing Plants and Where to Find Them,
by Ragthorn NettleDeath

If you think that any of these books might be of use to you at a later date, you may put them into your backpack now. Note down the titles of any books you take, then turn to **109**.

190

By turning to flee, you have made a fatal mistake. Before you can escape, a leaping Skeleton suddenly plunges its sword into your exposed back. The glittering blade pierces through to your heart, killing you instantly.

Your adventure has come to a swift end.

You suddenly notice a shortsword tucked into the belt of the guard. You duck under Faranen's attack and snatch the weapon from the unconscious man. The King surges towards you once more, swinging his blade in a fearsome, downward arc. Turn to **63**.

192

Just as he is about to leave, something makes Pelanthius halt in his tracks. "What is that noise?" he asks.

You realise that he is referring to the croaking sound that is coming from your pocket, so you show him the animal and explain where you found it.

The Wizard's eyes narrow suspiciously. "That is no ordinary toad," he says. "A strange curse surrounds it. I wonder if..." He pauses and asks you to put it in the palm of his hand, then he walks away with it, heading back into the trees. Perplexed, you set off after him. As you enter the wood, you see that he has placed the toad on the ground, and he is pointing his staff towards it.

The Wizard begins to mutter some magical words, then a gentle beam of light radiates from his staff and bathes the amphibian in a blue glow. To your amazement, its bumpy skin softens, then its features start to stretch and distort. In less than a minute, it has transformed into a beautiful young woman, who is wearing a flowing green dress.

The lady sways to her feet and falls into your arms. "Thank you!" she cries. "By all the Gods! Had you not picked me up in that cabin, lord knows how long I would have remained there!"

"Who are you?" you ask, looking somewhat shocked by this turn of events.

"I was kidnapped by the Witch several months ago," she explains, "whilst travelling by stage coach across the NightWind Moors. That hideous crone transformed me into a toad, then locked me up in her ghastly hut!"

"I have seen your face before," says Pelanthius. "Your father is a wealthy ruler who has been posting drawings of you across the land, offering a reward for your safe return. I suspect that the Witch was holding out for a ransom."

The woman begins to weep inconsolably, and it is clear that the whole experience has left her badly shaken.

Pelanthius assures her that she is now safe. "Come," he says, "let us find you some lodgings on the west side of town. In a few weeks, when I have finished helping my friend, I will return to RedBrook and take you back to your home. No reward will be necessary for my help."

She is overflowing with gratitude, and when she finally composes herself, she gives you each a blue necklace as a token of her appreciation. Remove the **Toad** from your Character Sheet, and add **Ariana's Necklace** to your list of possessions.

The woman is soon safely in her lodgings, and you are left to continue your quest. You split up and set off to explore different parts of the settlement.

Where do you want to go first?

If you want to make your way to The Wishing Well Tavern, turn to **101**.

If you would rather head for the shops in Lore Street, turn to **27**.

If you follow the signs towards Beggar's Lane, turn to **54**.

If you walk down Sword Street, turn to **38**.

Dawn breaks.

You wake, having slept well, and your muscles feel rejuvenated due to the comfortable bed. You walk onto the balcony and gaze out over the rooftops of Amossa. Although the sun is not yet in view, a blood red sky looms in the east, painting the fields beyond the city. You can hear the clinking march of soldiers in the streets, and you know that Faranen's army is readying itself for war.

You collect your belongings and are about to leave your room when the door suddenly opens. A palace guard has come to see you, bearing a final offering from the king. It is an oval **Amossan Shield**, which once belonged to the previous ruler of this city. It is a valuable gift, which feels sturdy and durable when strapped to your forearm. (Add the **Amossan Shield** to your list of belongings.)

You head out through the city's main gates, into the fields where the army is gathering.

From the west, a cold wind blows over the land, bringing with it the salt of the sea, and many banners flutter in the breeze. Men in shining armour stand in rows, swords unsheathed and ready for battle, and at the head of the army sits Pelanthius and king Faranen. They are both seated on white stallions, but the best horse has been reserved for you. It is a huge armoured steed, with a brave and fearless temperament. You climb into the saddle and position yourself alongside the king.

Faranen turns to face his men, his expression fierce and proud. "Today we ride into battle," he calls. "We will smash our way through the enemies who block the mountain pass, and we will destroy the gateway that has caused this chaos. It will not be easy, but we have a tough and hardy reputation, and today we will prove that we deserve it." He raises his shining sword into the air. "Now," he bellows, "let us make our way to that mountain, crush those wretches beneath our swords, and send them back to the Underworld in pieces!"

A roar goes up from the soldiers, thunderous and fierce, as they batter their swords against their shields. The king gives the order to march, and the army begins to move out across the dawn lit fields. The shadow of the Claw lies in the distance, and you move purposefully towards it.

Faranen turns to you with a stern expression. "We may meet some resistance on route to the mountain," he says, "but the fighting will not grow fierce until we reach the Valley of the Claw. Stay close to me, my friend. One way or another, we will reach that accursed Demon Gate." Turn to **126**.

194

Your opponent swings at you again, but this time you duck his attack. He is thrown off balance, so you surge forward and unleash a swift uppercut.

Roll one dice.

If you roll a six, turn to **16**.

If you roll any other number, turn to **81**.

Illustration Opposite

As you step outside, you see the red glow of the dawning sun, stretching over the rocky slopes. The war horse appears to have trotted off during the night, and you suspect that it has made its way back to town. But standing on the rocks, a short walk away, is the Wizard's horse. It is a huge and magnificent winged steed, with a mane as white as new snow. The feathers on its wings ruffle in the morning breeze, then it stomps the ground as if pleased to see you.

"Snowfire!" you exclaim, with a look of surprise.

The Wizard smiles. "Yes. It is something of a miracle that he is still alive considering all the trouble he gets himself into. Fighting a Dragon on his last adventure, of all the foolish things! But he made it home in the end."

"Well," you exclaim, "this is a fine sight for sore eyes! Now I know how you arrived so swiftly."

The Wizard nods with a smile. "Yes indeed. I am blessed to have him as a friend."

As you head towards the steed, Pelanthius pauses and looks to the south. A row of dark shapes are watching you from a ledge, half a mile away.

"Mountain Wolves," mutters the old Wizard. "They are residents of this region. Come, let us head off, before they come down the slope to cause us trouble."

Turn to **33**.

196

Although they look identical, you instinctively know that the left walkway should be avoided. It is unstable and might collapse into the lava if you walk on it, so you use the other crossing. Turn to **123**.

197

Your enemy collapses onto the floor and its body begins to shrivel and shrink. In a few moments, Kazal has returned to his normal form. Blood is oozing from his mouth, as he is close to death. You raise your sword, but you hesitate when you hear the sound of his weak voice. "Please," he says. "Do not strike. Spare me... and I will tell you whatever you want to know."

If you wish to strike him before he can utter another word, turn to **4**.

If you demand that he tells you the secret to defeating Evoka, turn to **184**.

198

The road you are following soon bends round and leads back into the town square.

If you have the word **Time** written on your Character Sheet, turn to **97**.

If not, turn to **15**.

199

As the man falls to the ground, Valantis suddenly appears around the corner. He has been alerted by the commotion, and he pauses when he sees you standing over the bodies of the two sailors. One man is dead, the other badly injured, and you suddenly realise it is you who looks like the villain! Valantis draws his sword, but you quickly tell him what happened. Fortunately, the wise old captain believes your story. He grabs the unconscious sailor and shakes him until he is awake.

"I've had trouble from you before, Morkus," Valantis tells the man. "You talked yourself out of it last time, and I gave you a second chance, but my patience has run out. Thieving and thuggery won't be tolerated on the WindRunner, not while I'm in charge." He drags the sailor up onto the deck and hurls him overboard, telling him to swim home. You make a note not to annoy the old sea captain, then you head to your bunk for the night. Turn to **84**.

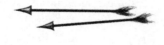

200

Together, the defenders begin to hack their way towards the Necromancer. Too late do you realise that you have fallen into a trap. Your enemy's power has not diminished at all, and he has succeeded in luring you into the open. The undead suddenly swell in number and you find yourself besieged. Men fall around you, and you are unable to batter your way back to the safety of the town. You are eventually cut down by the horde, along with the rest of the men.

The defence of Mosal has failed.

After a while, the path begins to widen. You enter a stretch of road filled with market stalls, and the area is bustling with people despite the late hour. You see nefarious traders selling a host of unpleasant wares, including live animals in small cages, then a thin man bumps into you and tries to sell you a bag of rotten meat.

You shake your head. "I am looking for the harbour," you say. "Can you give me directions?"

"Pah! Find it yourself," he snaps, before hobbling away on his wooden leg.

You continue past the market, then the lane narrows and becomes quiet once more. It is not long before you see the body of a man laying face down in a side turning, with a dagger protruding from his back. He was robbed several days ago, and his corpse has been left for the rats.

"This is a grisly place indeed," mutters Pelanthius.

You eventually halt at a T-junction. Loud voices echo from both directions. A wooden arrow bearing the picture of a ship points left.

If you follow the sign, turn to **236**.

If you turn right, turn to **267**.

The shopkeeper's eyes are beady and dark, and you are unsure if you like the look of him. He ignores your question and continues reading. Upon his desk is a strange lantern with a tiny orb of golden light flittering around behind the glass. "What is this?" you ask.

"A Tree Fairy," mutters the man, sounding rather aloof and wearied by your presence. "I caught it and put it in the lantern as a source of light. It is useful to have on my desk when I'm reading."

The Fairy is so small that you can barely make out its little wings and body. You sense that the creature is filled with sadness, trapped in its tiny glass cage.

Pelanthius has now disappeared through a narrow door into another part of the shop, and you can hear him shuffling through scrolls and muttering to himself.

If you want to distract the shopkeeper and set the Fairy free, turn to **217**.

If you offer to buy the Fairy, turn to **179**.

If you leave the shop, turn to **53**.

203

Following the woman's advice, you make your way to the shop. It is an old building with a missing sign, and the tall, scrawny owner nods as you enter. He is dressed in dark clothes with patches over his eyes. A crow sits silently upon his shoulder, watching you with gleaming, black orbs.

Below are the items which catch your attention; amend your Character Sheet as necessary.

Items you might like to buy:

An **Enchanted, Emerald Bracelet**, said to bring
luck (One available) Cost: **six Crimson Coins**

Enchanted, Spiked Climbing Boots
(One pair available) Cost: **four Crimson Coins**

Magic Gloves
(One pair available) Cost: **five Crimson Coins**

Items you might like to sell:

If you possess a **Tarnished Gem**
the trader will offer you **two Crimson Coins** for it

If you have a **Small Goblin Statue**
he will buy it for **three Crimson Coins**

For a **Small Fairy Statue**
he will offer **three Crimson Coins**

For a **Sapphire Ring**
he will give you **four Crimson Coins**

For **Ariana's Necklace**
he will give you **six Crimson Coins**

For a **Black Crystal Necklace**
he will give you **six Crimson Coins**

When you are done, turn to **361**.

204

You continue down a gradually widening street, and you eventually find yourself at the docks, where two merchant vessels are moored. One is named The WindRunner, the other is called The Sea Star. Rough looking men with greasy hair are loading crates onto the ships, so you ask them where the vessels are heading.

"Both ships are bound for Port Acura," answers one of the men. "Each is loaded with different goods, and they are due to set sail in the morning."

If you ask to see the captain of The WindRunner, turn to **171**.

If you ask to see the captain of The Sea Star, turn to **239**.

205

You explore the tunnels beneath the tower. Some merely lead to empty rooms, while others circle around and return you to the point where you started. Despite your initial lack of success, you feel compelled to keep looking.

If you have the special ability of **Greater Wisdom**, turn to **168**.

If not, you must roll one dice to see if luck is on your side.

If you roll a six, turn to **96**.

If you roll any other number, you do not discover anything of interest, so you decide to set off on your quest, turn to **26**.

206

You shield yourself with your arm, sparing your face from the impact, then you retaliate with a fierce punch to the man's ribs. As he staggers backwards, an unknown assailant grabs you from behind, lifts you up and hurls you over the top of the nearby bar. You land on your back and crack your head on the ale soaked floorboards. (Reduce your **Life Force** by one point.)

If you are still alive, turn to **237**.

207

You open the compartment, but it appears empty. You reach deep inside, where the shadows are thickest, and your fingers touch a cold object. You have discovered a sapphire ring. It is not magical, but it is a beautiful item.

If you wish to take it, add the **Sapphire Ring** to your list of possessions, then turn to **332**.

208

Several Amossans attempt to block the creature's path, but the undead menace smashes straight through their ranks! To your horror, the skeletal monstrosity spears Faranen in the chest, knocking him from his horse.

Several Amossans shout out in dismay. "Faranen has fallen!" yells one. "Vengeance for the King!" bellows another. A group of soldiers rush forward to attack the Giant, but they are beaten to the ground and hurled aside like woven dolls. The beast now begins wading towards you, carving a path of destruction straight through the Amossan ranks. You may have no choice but to fight this horror after all! Turn to **162**.

Pelanthius agrees to your plan, then he strides off, leaving you to explore the side turning. As you move towards the building, you become aware of a loud commotion. You step through the door and see that a wild brawl is taking place. Chairs and tables are flying through the air, while rough looking men – drunk beyond reason – are hurling punches and throwing each other around the room. You decide to step back through the exit, but you are suddenly set upon by a drunken fool armed with a chair leg.

Roll one dice to see if luck is on your side. If you roll a three or less, you are struck across the head before you can duck: lose one **Life force**. If you roll a four or higher, you dodge the attack and knock the man unconscious with a massive punch to the jaw.

If you are still alive, turn to **146**.

"Head down the lane and look for DarkThorn's shop," she advises. "It's an untidy mess, but he has some interesting items. His Emerald Bracelet would prove a wise purchase for an adventurer, but don't waste your money on those so called Magic Gloves. They're fake, nothing magic about them, and they'll only serve to lighten your coin pouch. DarkThorn is blind, but don't be fooled; he can see through the eyes of his crow, and he'll be watching your every move."

She gives you directions and bids you farewell. You thank her before returning to the lane. Turn to **203**.

Amidst the skirmish, a grim, expressionless man appears ahead of you. He is nearly seven feet tall, thin and bony, with pupilless eyes. He is a ghastly vision, dressed all in black, with a serrated blade gripped in his hand. He is the surgeon of the enemy ship, feared even by his own shipmates.

(Torayus only leaves the bowels of his vessel at night. His skin is pale, and his appearance sings of Vampiric lineage. Indeed, more than once has a deckhand vanished mysteriously on Blood-Gor's ship.)

You must fight!

TORAYUS, THE SADISTIC SURGEON

LIFE FORCE   10   STRIKING SPEED 9

Focus	Move	Damage
1	Life Draining Stare	1
2-3	Sweeping Blade	2
4-5	Slashing Blade	2
6	Blood Toothed Bite	See Below*

(*Special Move: If you are struck by the Surgeon's Blood Toothed Bite, turn immediately to 330.)

If you win, turn to **44**.

212

One item in particular catches your interest. A strange shape, carved from bone, has been attached to a loop of string, so that it can be worn around the neck. It glitters as you lift it, and it warms the palm of your hand.

"What is this?" you ask.

"It will bring you luck," says the shopkeeper. "Something we could all do with, in these dark times."

The item costs an eye-watering **eight Crimson Coins**, but if you helped Cirian to carry the boxes, she will sell it to you for half that price.

If you want to buy it, add the **Glittering Bone Charm** to your list of possessions, then adjust your money accordingly.

When you are done, you leave the shop.

If you return to Pelanthius and press on towards the palace, turn to **103**.

If you continue to explore the Merchant's Quarter, turn to **294**.

The realistic little figurine, which is made of dark stone, bears a striking resemblance to a grinning Goblin. (If you want to take it, add the **Small Goblin Statue** to your list of possessions.) You also notice a switch on the wall next to the fireplace.

If you want to flick the switch, to see what happens, turn to **92**.

Otherwise, return to page **148** and choose an option that you have not yet picked.

214

You show the moss to the alchemist. The man looks stunned, and he immediately begins to scrutinise it. "What luck is this?!" he says. "I'll give you four crimson coins, if you will part with it."

You consider this a good trade, so you agree to his offer. (Remove the **Pink Moss** from your Character Sheet, then add **four Crimson Coins** to your belongings.)

The shopkeeper looks very happy indeed, and he immediately goes back to his work, leaving you to browse the merchandise. Turn to **311**.

She tells you to stare into her eyes, so you do as she asks. A nearby candle flutters momentarily, though no breeze is present. Your body begins to feel weak, and a strange sensation washes through your veins. You have a feeling that the old woman is reading your mind.

"So," she whispers, ever so softly. "You are the one that I have been seeking... good... good... do not struggle… it will all be over soon."

You suddenly realise that your muscles are not responding. You are gripped by her hypnotic stare, and you cannot move.

"Age has robbed me of my splendour," she mutters. "But not for much longer. The Spirit Winds told me you might come, and in return for your death they promised me the secrets of eternal youth. My potion will soon be perfected, and no longer will I be trapped in this ancient shell of a body."

You are vaguely aware of her hand, pulling a knife from beneath her clothes. As she raises it above her head, you muster the willpower to break her gaze. You push yourself backwards and crash to the floor, narrowly avoiding the swish of her blade. Turn to **230**.

You raise your arms to shield your face, then you leap backwards, narrowly avoiding the sweep of his second punch.

If you smash your fist into Ugluk's ribs, turn to **342**.
If you maintain your defensive strategy, turn to **194**.

"My friend, the Wizard, is taking a long time," you mutter. "I guess he is looking for something specific."

The shopkeeper puts down his book and skulks into the other room, to see if Pelanthius needs any help.

When he has gone, you loosen the catch on the lantern and open the glass. The little light suddenly sweeps out and whooshes around the room, knocking scrolls from shelves and sending paper flying into the air. The shopkeeper runs back in, waving his arms in a panic. The Fairy darts left and right, sending several books crashing to the ground, then it flies out through the door, leaving a terrible mess in its wake. The angry shopkeeper pushes you outside, accusing you of freeing his pet, then he slams the door and warns you not to come back in. After he has gone, you see a little glow descending from the sky. The Fairy floats up to you and taps you gently on the nose. The little creature has just cast a spell of gratitude, and you feel suddenly light-headed. Magic briefly glitters in the air, then you begin to feel unusually calm: increase your **Life Force** by three points. The Fairy then flutters away, back to the distant woods where it belongs.

Turn to **53**.

As the tentacle comes close, you seize the initiative and swing your blade, slicing into your enemy.

Turn to **251** to finish the fight with your sword, but reduce your opponent's **Life Force** immediately by six points, due to your sword and arrow strikes.

219

You avoid the blow, and the brute accidentally strikes the man behind you, knocking several teeth from his jaw. You turn and force your way to the door, then you burst back into the open.

To your surprise, Pelanthius is standing outside, looking concerned. "I did not get far when I sensed that you were in trouble, so I came back as quickly as I could," he says. "Are you okay?"

"I can understand the lure of a warm tavern, but I am not too keen on this one," you tell him. "We'll get nothing but a black eye in this place."

You decide to explore further down the lane.

Turn to **133**.

Illustration Opposite

You spin around to defend the besieged man. Three Skeletons have set upon him and you must fight them all at once!

SKELETONS

LIFE FORCE	15	STRIKING SPEED	7

Focus	Move	Damage
1	Claws of Bone	1
2-3	Blade Strike	2
4-5	Thrusting Spear	2
6	Hacking Sword	2

If you win, you quickly help the man to his feet. Turn to **25**.

221

As you approach the tower, a spark of energy leaps from the stone and burns your skin. It is as if the building could sense your intentions.

(Reduce your **Life Force** by one point.)

Pelanthius raises an eyebrow. "You'll not break into a Wizard's tower, if that's what you were thinking," he says. "Powerful spells protect it."

If you sit by the tower and wait for the owner to return, turn to **14**.

If you explore RedBrook, in the hope of finding Kazal there, turn to **93**.

Your fist slams into Ugluk's nose, drawing blood, but the monstrous fighter barely seems to notice. He retaliates with a mighty jab which sends you staggering back across the platform. (Reduce your **Life Force** by two more points.) If you are still alive, turn to **194**.

The warm interior is a pleasant reprieve from the deepening night.

"You do not look like you come from these parts," she says.

You nod. "I am a traveller. I only recently set foot here."

"Well, you've picked a bad time to come to Amossa," she says. "The dead haunt the shadows beyond the city while King Faranen sits idly upon his throne. He has been a good King until now, but of late he has fallen silent. Anyhow, what is it that brings you to the merchant's sector?"

"I am looking for items that might be of use to an adventurer?"

She shakes her head. "I have nothing of that ilk in my shop, but I do know a place that might interest you. I could give you some information, for a small fee of course. It might end up saving you some time and money, if you are wise enough to listen." She holds out her hand.

If you want to hear what she has to say, remove a **Crimson Coin** from your belongings, then turn to **210**.

If you bid her farewell and leave, turn to **373**.

224

You have a sinking feeling that your journey through the mirror may have set you on a path to failure. However, if one last battle is to be fought, then you will not hide in the shadows.

"There is always hope until the end," you tell yourself. You swing into the empty saddle of a steed, which was tethered to the group, then you set off with the riders, into the north.

Turn to **341**.

225

(If you paid the Fortune Teller, you take back the coin which you placed on the table). Your immediate surroundings reveal nothing of interest, however, you do discover a hatchway hidden beneath a rug. Pulling it open, you see a flight of wooden steps descending into a dimly lit, shadow haunted cellar. You are about to investigate when you hear a loud knock at the front door. It is probably another customer. There will be a lot of explaining to do if you are discovered, so you remain quiet. The newcomer eventually leaves, and you listen to their footsteps fading away down the alley.

If you descend the stairs, turn to **115**.

If you leave and return to the ship, turn to **338**.

226

"I have lived for nearly eight hundred years," she croaks, "and in that time I have learnt a thing or two about the world. From the safety of my home I have spied on friends and enemies alike, watching people through my crystal ball. My mind has come to know many things." She pauses and grins darkly. You cannot tell what she is thinking, but she seems to take great pride in her crooked accomplishments. Turn to **12**.

227

Each one houses a severed hand, which is floating in embalming fluid. It seems that many an unfortunate visitor has met their end in this house of horrors. If you want to keep searching, you must pick an option that you have not yet chosen.

If you examine the trinkets, turn to **39**.

If you investigate the mysterious chalk markings, turn to **297**.

If you are ready to leave, turn to **129**.

228

You suddenly hear floorboards creaking, two floors up. A customer has entered the building via the front door, and you hear them gasp with surprise. They have discovered the deceased owner. You do not want to be seen down here in the cellar, as you have no time to explain what happened. Pulling a tapestry from the wall, you uncover another opening. Fortunately, it leads to a flight of steps that head upwards. You decide to see where they lead, and you soon come up through another hatch, into a shady side street. After the events in WrettleNeck's grisly house, you decide it would be wise to return to the ship and get some rest.

Turn to **338**.

229

Having returned to the street, you quickly scan the clouds. Fortunately, the Dragon is nowhere in sight.

Several men suddenly run past you, all armed with swords. One of them halts at your side, panting and out of breath. "We need fighters," he says. "I see that you have a weapon. Word has it that the main gate is about to fall. We cannot let those things get inside the walls, or we will all be doomed. Quickly, follow me!"

The man is right. If the enemy break into the town, the situation will become even more desperate. Having failed to escape through the tunnels, you decide to return to the main gate and help the defenders. At least there you may be of some use. Turn to **130**.

230

The old woman has no intention of letting you escape her abode. She scrambles over the table, trying to stab you before you can defend yourself!

DERANGED FORTUNE TELLER

LIFE FORCE 6   STRIKING SPEED 7

Focus	Move	Damage
1	Throttling Grip	1
2-3	Sweeping Blade	2
4-5	Psychotic Frenzy	2
6	Depraved Curse	4

If you win, turn to **247**.

231

Withered branches, like long fingers, suddenly close in over the path, blocking your passage. You have no time to waste, so you rush forward and charge into the barrier, smashing through it with the force of your momentum.

(Reduce your **Life Force** by two points.)

You almost tumble to the ground, but somehow you manage to keep your footing. Turn to **57**.

232

You stagger towards your steed and drag yourself back into the saddle. The grim spectres have returned to the clouds. They look down, snarling with dissatisfaction at your continued existence.

Before Faranen can ask if you are okay, you turn towards him with an urgent expression. "The enemy approaches," you exclaim. "A skeletal army is about to attack from the front and sides. Tell your men to ready their shields!" Turn to **73**.

233

It does not take long to find Valantis. He is sitting at a table in the middle of the room, drinking a huge tankard of ale with one hand, whilst arm wrestling with the other. After a swift victory, you see him quaff his drink, then he heads back to the bar for another. He is a short fellow, but he has a brutish physique, with powerful, broad shoulders and huge, gnarled hands. He has a thick black beard with several streaks of grey, and his weather-beaten skin looks rugged and leathery. Pelanthius sits beside him and strikes up a conversation, then the Wizard hands him a weighty pouch of coins. The captain's eyes sparkle merrily and he instantly agrees to let you travel with him. He shoves the pouch into a hidden pocket beneath his coat, finishes his second drink, then leans forward so that only you and the Wizard can hear him.

"Come," he says, "we had best not linger here any longer. Some devious rogues just witnessed our trade. Thieves are abound in Port Kattaran, and their eyes are everywhere. We had best take our leave and head to the ship."

You follow him outside, then you quickly turn west into another lane. However, you soon hear footfalls approaching, and you realise that three men have followed you out of the tavern. With predatory expressions, they rush forward to attack!

A blast of light springs from Pelanthius's staff, knocking one of the villains off of his feet. Valantis leaps at the second ambusher, whilst you deal with the third.

ROGUE

LIFE FORCE 8   STRIKING SPEED 7

Focus	Move	Damage
1	Punch	1
2-3	Devious Grapple	2
4-5	Sweeping Strike	2
6	Stabbing Blade	2

If you win, turn to **305**.

234

On closer inspection, you see that each bird has not two, but three gleaming eyes. Their wings are spread wide and their little beaks are open, as if frozen in time. For some reason you feel compelled to reach towards them. As soon as your finger touches one of the black wings, the animal begins to move. Your action has awoken it from a dark spell, and it immediately breaks free from the string that was suspending it. As it flaps around the room, the others also stir to life. You are suddenly surrounded by beating wings, pecking beaks and raking claws, as they try to bash past you towards the exit. (Lose one **Life Force**.) You raise your arms to defend yourself, then they vanish through the hatchway and soar to freedom up the crooked chimney.

If you have not yet done so, you may now examine:

The trinkets, turn to **39**.

The bowls, turn to **227**.

Or the markings on the floor, turn **297**.

When you are ready to leave, turn to **129**.

235

You take the box out of her arms and carry it into her storeroom. It is quite heavy, and you can see why she was struggling. She is grateful for the aid, and you move four more boxes, to save her the trouble. When you are done, she reaches into her pocket and hands you **two Crimson Coins**.

"I was happy to help," you tell her. " I did not expect money in return."

"Which is why you should have it," she says. "Kind gestures, such as yours, are not as common as they should be."

If you accept her offering, add the coins to your belongings. You then scan the shelves. Turn to **212**.

236

The lane soon opens into a wide, cobbled courtyard. A group of people are hurling stones, as well as insults, at a cage that is hanging from a wooden contraption in the middle of the area. A man sits behind the bars, dressed in rags, protecting himself with his arms. After a few minutes, once the crowd's anger has died down, they disperse, leaving you and Pelanthius alone with the prisoner. The scrawny man peers at you from between the bars with a sad expression.

"By the Gods," he says, "spare some pity for me, strangers." He waves you over to his cage, with weary, pleading eyes.

If you approach him, and ask what deed led to his incarceration, turn to **263**.

If you continue on, into the next lane, turn to **282**.

237

Rough hands grab you. You are too dazed to understand what is happening, but you are dragged back over the bar and into the fray. You regain your senses just in time to see an elbow sweeping towards your head.

If you have had enough of this place, you may duck and surge towards the exit, turn to **219**.

If you block, then punch your attacker in the jaw, turn to **246.**

238

As you step back from the crowd, the female arm wrestler suddenly slams her opponent's hand down onto the table. A roar goes up from the spectators, they become very animated, and you are almost knocked to the ground by an over-excited fool who is leaping around the courtyard.

Numerous lanes branch out from this area, so you pick one at random and head off to explore elsewhere.

Turn to **204**.

Two sailors are arm wrestling by the gangplank of The Sea Star, so you wait for the competition to finish before asking to see their captain. The winner introduces himself as the ship's cook.

"Sure," he grins, "I'll introduce ya to him, but only if you can beat me in an arm wrestle."

Pelanthius gives you an encouraging nod, so you lean your elbow on a crate and grip the cook's hand. Your opponent is a large man and, when the contest begins, you are surprised by the immensity of his strength.

Suddenly, the Wizard taps his staff discreetly against your foot. A surge of power momentarily fills your veins, and your opponent's eyes bulge with horror as you slam his hand down onto the wood.

"By the Gods!" says the loser. "You have the strength of an Ogre!"

A tall man, who was watching from the ship's deck, comes down the gangplank towards you. He has a missing eye, long black hair, and a cold stare. "I am the captain," he says. "Fornax is my name. What do you want from me?"

Pelanthius introduces himself. "My friend and I need to reach Port Acura," he says, "and I am willing to pay well for our board." He hands over a heavy pouch of coins, and the captain quickly takes it with a greedy expression.

"Well," says Fornax, counting the contents. "I'm sure I can find some space on board. I'll have a deckhand show you to your bunks."

Pelanthius heads onto the ship and goes straight to bed, leaving you with the captain. "Go explore more of the town if you want," he says. "I can tell you where the gambling dens are, just make sure you are back by first light, as the tide waits for no one."

Looking around, you notice a narrow alley nearby, with a black door at its end. Your eyes are drawn to it, and you see a sign on the wall which reads: *Madame WrettleNeck, Fortune Teller for hire*.

If you want to visit the Fortune Teller, turn to **322**.

If you want to visit the gambling dens, turn to **389**.

If you want to sleep, turn to **338**.

240

They are mystical symbols, and each one is surrounded by a white circle. You are no expert in the art of dark magic, but you gather that the fortune teller was trying to enact some kind of ritual, in her doomed pursuit of eternal youth. You must now pick an option that you have not yet chosen.

If you take a closer look at the stuffed birds, which have been carefully positioned above the chalk drawings, turn to **234**.

If you examine the trinkets, turn to **80**.

If you look inside the bowls, turn to **306**.

If you are ready to leave, turn to **129**.

241

Determined to win, you unleash a sudden barrage of attacks. Ugluk is too busy protecting himself to retaliate, and you strike him in the temple with a wild punch. The brute is dazed, and he loses his footing and falls over the edge of the platform. He lands face down on the floorboards, and a sudden cheer erupts from the crowd! Turn to **391**.

242

As you approach the trees, their branches reach towards you. Fortunately, you are too quick to be caught, and you dodge past them. Turn to **57**.

243

"I thought I heard a noise," mutters Pelanthius, quizzically. Then he shakes his head. "I must have been imagining things," he says, before striding out of the door. You are about to follow him when you hear a deep croak resonate throughout the hut. You turn around and see the toad watching you from the bookshelf. It is staring at you with its leafy green eyes, and for a brief moment you are convinced that it has a sad expression..

If you want to take the creature with you, turn to **24**.

If you would rather leave it where it is, turn to **195**.

244

You halt outside the next shop. A sign above the door reads *Cirian's Enchanted Items.* Looking through the entrance, you see necklaces hanging from shelves. Each item is sparkling with traces of magic. The owner, a slender young women with blonde hair, is carrying a box towards the storeroom at the back of the shop. She is clearly struggling, and her cheeks are flushed. "Welcome," she says in a friendly voice, sounding slightly out of breath. "I'll be with you shortly. Feel free to look around."

If you offer to help her, turn to **235**.

If you let her continue, whilst you browse the merchandise, turn to **212**.

If you walk on, turn to **294**.

245

The smashed armour falls apart and crashes onto the floor. Kazal cannot believe that you are still alive. You see dark shadows forming around his eyes, then you realise that his magical deeds are starting to tire him. You grasp your sword and spring forward, but you have only taken three paces when he slams the base of his staff onto the ground. Six ghostly daggers appear in the air above his head, all glowing with a misty blue light, and at his command they shoot towards you.

If you try to smash the daggers aside with your sword, turn to **82**.

If you try to duck under the flying blades, turn to **381**.

246

Your opponent stumbles backwards, dazed by your punch. However, he is a huge figure, probably the largest fellow in the tavern, and he quickly shakes himself to his senses. Before you can act, he grabs you and lifts you into the air. You are hurled over the heads of the other fighters, then you crash through a window and land in the street.

When your vision clears, you see Pelanthius staring down at you with a raised eyebrow.

"I did not get far when I sensed that you were in trouble, so I came back as quickly as I could," he says. "Are you okay?"

You groan and clamber to your feet. "I can understand the lure of a warm tavern, but I am not too fond of this one," you tell him. "We'll get nothing but a black eye in this place." You decide to explore further down the lane. Turn to **133**.

247

The crazed woman lies dead at your feet, the knife still resting in her hand.

If you want to get out of this place, you can race back to the ship by turning to **338**.

If you want to search the room, turn to **225**.

248

You give chase through the shadowy alleys. The wicked Thief is a fast runner, but you are determined to catch him.

If you have the special ability of **Haste**, turn to **19**.

If not, turn to **114**.

249

One of Fornax's men enters the room behind you. "I have checked the rest of the ship," he says. "No bodies, just bloodstains everywhere. The cargo is missing, and she is listing and taking on water."

A woeful creak, from the damaged hull, moves through the vessel, but it sounds more like the gentle cry of weeping souls.

"We had best leave," he says. "I do not think it would be wise to stay on this crumbling ship any longer."

You clamber back into the longboat and return to The Sea Star.

"What did you discover?" asks Fornax sternly.

"No crew, just blood everywhere," you respond.

"Pirates," spits the captain. "We had best keep the crow's nest manned day and night. And I will tell the crew to be vigilant. Too many lookouts are better than too few."

You watch as the doomed vessel slowly sinks into its watery grave, then you sail onwards. The stars soon begin to shimmer on the rolling waves, so you head below deck to have supper with the sailors. You are greeted by a bowl of slop. It has little nutritional value but it suppresses your hunger.

The hour has now grown late, so you decide to get some rest. Turn to **84**.

250

You swiftly load an arrow and fire upwards.

Roll one dice to see if luck is on your side.

If you roll a three or less, turn to **278**.

If you roll a four or higher, turn to **262**.

TENTACLE

LIFE FORCE 12   STRIKING SPEED 8

Focus	Move	Damage
1	Spray Of Acid Blood	2
2-3	Hurl The Enemy	2
4-5	Sweeping Clout	3
6	Thrashing Rage	4

If you win, turn to **147**.

252

The dreaded scoundrel of the high seas falls dead at your feet, but the other Pirates keep on fighting. Maybe they have not realised that their captain is dead, or maybe they do not care; either way the clash continues. The villains are eager to get their hands on the goods that are stored in The Sea Star's hold, so they are not about to give up easily.

Roll one dice to determine which villainous crew member you must confront next.

If you roll a one, turn to **211**.

If you roll a two, turn to **348**.

If you roll a three, turn to **326**.

If you roll a four, turn to **66**.

If you roll a five, turn to **288**.

If you roll a six, turn to **275**.

253

You pause, sensing danger.

Eerie laughter echos from the skull's rattling jaws, then beams of searing light suddenly leap from its eye sockets. You duck the rays, then, a second later, the skull explodes with a calamitous bang. You are knocked from your feet by the force of the blast, and a huge crack appears in the stonework overhead. The roof tumbles down into the water, but you push yourself backwards and escape the deluge. When the dust has settled, you see that the left tunnel has been completely blocked.

If you explore the tunnel to your right, turn to **277**.

If you climb up through the hole that has been left in the ceiling, turn to **229**.

254

(Remove another **Arrow** from your inventory.)

You find your mark, and more blood splashes onto the ship. But this time you have gained the creature's attention. It releases its hold on the mast and suddenly swings towards you, trying to knock you into the sea. You dive onto the deck, narrowly avoiding the attack, then you leap to your feet. Two sailors rush to your aid, lancing the enemy with boat hooks, but the blood soaked tentacle sweeps around and knocks them both over the side. One of the men vanishes into the waves, while the second grabs the edge of the vessel and is left dangling from the ship.

If you leap forward to help him, turn to **291**.

If you spring at the tentacle with your sword raised, turn to **218**.

255

Along with five other men, you clamber into a longboat and row across the choppy water. Fornax remains on The Sea Star, and you can see him watching from the stern. You head to the listing ship and climb up onto the deck. There is no sign of life, and the wheel is turning eerily by itself, at the mercy of the waves.

"What witchcraft is this?" mutters a man, as he climbs up behind you. He draws his dagger, heads forward, and tentatively peers into the open hatchway that leads into the belly of the ship. He watches as you head downwards, but does not follow. The interior is dark, and you can hear nothing but the creaking of the timbers. You draw your sword and move deeper, towards the back of the vessel, then you push through a broken door which leads into the captain's cabin. A navigation table sits ahead of you and a log book rests on the floor. Bloodstains cover the walls and even the ceiling, but there is no sign of any bodies.

If you pick up the book, turn to **280**.

If you investigate the navigation table, turn to **317**.

256

As you loose the second arrow, your adversary suddenly twists its body. You can no longer see its underbelly, only its gleaming, tough scales. Your arrow shatters against its natural armour, then the serpent sweeps forward, its fangs dripping with venom!

Remove the fired **Arrow** from your belongings, then turn to **290**.

257

The tree trunk soars over your head, narrowly missing you, but the branches catch your bow and tear it from your hand. You look up and see the colossal humanoid bearing down on you. You can retrieve your bow after the fight, but you have no time to do so now. You roll to the left, narrowly avoiding a savage punch, then you are forced to draw your sword to defend yourself. Turn to **49** to fight your enemy, but reduce its **Life Force** immediately by two points, due to the damage caused by your ranged attack.

258

Your fingers find a nick in the wooden deck and, despite the acute angle, you are able to stop yourself from falling. Someone tumbles past you, but you grab them with your spare hand, clinging onto them with all your might. All across the ship, the sailors are grabbing hold of anything they can, to stop themselves from tumbling down into the sea. The situation is becoming more desperate by the second, as the ship is continuing to lean at an ever increasing angle. Lightening blazes across the sky, illuminating the chaotic scene. Then, down amongst the waves, you see a monstrous mouth emerging from the black sea: huge teeth, a gaping vortex of a maw, and countless, unblinking eyes.

Suddenly, Pelanthius's head pokes up through the hatchway behind you, looking somewhat shocked and ruffled. A beam of light instantly erupts from his staff and soars over the deck. It then arches downwards and strikes the head of the sea beast.

The monster falls silent and ceases its attack. The Wizard's magic has not wounded it; instead, the spell has put it to sleep. The mega beast drifts down into the depths of the sea, then the WindRunner rights itself and surges loose from the deadly embrace.

Turn to **268**.

259

Your arrow thuds into the shoulder of the rushing figure. (Remove it from your inventory.) The man grunts, and you see the pain etched briefly in his face. He then leaps close, his weapons blazing through the air. You stagger backwards and draw your sword, parrying his sweeping blade.

Turn to **284** to engage in close combat, but reduce your opponent's **Life Force** by two points, due to the damage caused by your arrow.

Illustration Opposite

You clamber down into a small, square room. The only light comes through the opening above you, so it is very dark indeed. Several tapestries hang from the walls, depicting strange constellations. In the centre of the chamber is a table draped in black cloth. An ornate goblet sits upon it, filled with dark liquid. To your left, you see a tall mirror that is glittering with traces of magic.

If you quench your thirst, turn to **323**.

If you investigate the mirror, turn to **345**.

If you decide to leave, turn to **228**.

261

The sailor's eyes narrow and he spits on the floor. "He is one of the three Pirate Kings," he tells you. "A trading vessel like ours has no desire to meet him out on the high seas, but if he comes near me I'll cut him a new smile from ear to ear." He goes back to drinking his ale. You can tell that he has no desire to talk further of it, so you step into the tavern. Turn to **233**.

The arrow thuds into the creature's neck, and the beast releases a thunderous roar. It grabs the protruding shaft, tears it free and crushes it into dust with its hand.

(Remove one **Arrow** from your belongings.)

Your enemy suddenly opens its mouth, exhaling forcefully. A freezing wind surges from its lungs, and you roll to the left to avoid the blast. Glancing over your shoulder, you see that the trees have been turned to ice behind you!

If you leap to your feet and release a second arrow, turn to **281**.

If you draw your sword and rush at your enemy, turn to **269**.

As you step up to the cage, the man's expression suddenly changes, revealing his wicked intentions. His arms spring out between the bars, then he grabs your throat and drags you against the gibbet, strangling you with his filthy hands. Fortunately, you are far stronger than the wretched villain, so you quickly break free and stagger backwards.

Turn to **282**.

As you turn to exit the room, you see that the door is slowly closing behind you. You grab the handle, pull it open, and step back into the night. The old woman hurries to the entrance. She calls after you, urging you to return, but to no avail. Leaving the alley, you make your way back to the gangplank by The Sea Star.

If you wish to head onto the ship and go to bed, turn to **338**.

If you would rather investigate the gambling dens on the north side of town, turn to **366**.

265

"Save your pity for another day," he says coldly. "They are marauders from the wild. Murderers and worse. Their raiding party swept into town a few days ago, but they quickly realised they had picked the wrong people to ambush. This port is a rough and ready place. Let the Hanging Bridge be a warning to others."

He steps aside so that you may pass, then he returns to his watch.

Turn to **298**.

You find yourself walking down another lane, but your passage is soon blocked by a mound of junk which rises up to the rooftops. You start to climb it, and you are almost at the top when you notice a tunnel leading into the heart of the debris. To your surprise, a skinny old man clambers out of it. He is clothed in rags, his white hair is a mess, and you can see by his wild expression that he is completely mad.

"Don't you be causing any trouble on my hill!" he says, "or I'll set my pet on you! Look at him! Look how ferocious he is!" he exclaims, pointing at nothing but thin air. He then begins dancing around, before laying down and rolling in circles. You decide to make your escape, but he jumps up and blocks your way. "Wait," he says, "I have something to sell you, but I can't tell you what it is. You can have it for the price of three, invisible, red rubies."

He will not let you be, so you hold out your empty hand and pretend to drop three invisible rubies into his palm. He looks ecstatic, then he disappears back into the tunnel and starts to search around inside the junk pile. Moments later, he begins to argue with himself; his temper flares, and crashing sounds reverberate out of the hole.

If you take this opportunity to escape over the hilltop, turn to **336**.

If you wait, turn to **312**.

The lane soon opens into the town square, where a group of hardy looking people have formed a circle around two arm wrestlers. A slim but muscular man, wearing face piercings and a sleeveless top, is locked in a contest with a brutish, stocky woman. Her chunky arms are covered in tattoos, and her face bears a snarl that would put a shiver into any opponent. Both contestants are straining and red-faced, yet neither seem to have the better of the other.

"Break his arm, Berty," shouts a toothless man to your left. "Show him what you're made of."

"Come on Torrik, you fool!" yells another, in an angry voice, "I bet three coins on you man, put some effort into it!"

A thin little creature with blue skin is taking money from people in the crowd. "Double or nothing," he shouts. "Three crimmies is the maximum you can bet. Think ya know who'll win? Well put ya money where ya mouth is."

If you do not wish to gamble, turn to **238**.

If you want to place a bet (and can afford to do so), you must first decide who you think will win.

If you think Berty will be the victor, turn to **279**.

If you think Torrik will win, turn to **289**.

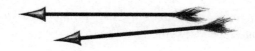

Valantis staggers towards the Wizard, looking red-faced and out of breath. "Well done, Grey Beard," he says, sounding both grateful and angry in the same instant. "I owe you my life, but make your presence known quicker next time!"

You begin to help the wounded, but after a few minutes a flustered crewman appears through the hatchway, claiming that the ship is taking on water. With a worried look, you follow Valantis below deck to assess the extent of the damage.

Roll one dice.

If you roll a six, turn to **368**.

If you roll any other number, turn to **167**.

269

You charge forward, your blade gleaming in the moonlight.

Turn to **49** to engage in close combat, but reduce your opponent's **Life Force** by two points, due to the damage caused by your arrow.

270

You soon come to an open door with a sign that reads: *The West Wind Tavern*. The smell of ale and sweat drifts out, and you can hear rowdy laughter within. Two men are standing outside; the same duo who you overheard near the arm wrestling match.

You approach them and ask if they know of any ships that are heading to Port Acura. They do not seem particularily interested in talking, as they have just bought themselves some tankards of ale, but they spare you a few moments. "Conversation eats into our drinking time," says one of them. "Head inside and speak to our captain, Valantis. His ship is bound for Port Acura in a few hours."

"Are you looking to join us for the journey?" asks the second man.

You nod, then he continues to speak. "Valantis will charge you a fee for sure, but we could always do with a Wizard and another sword arm on board."

They turn away and begin drinking from their tankards.

If you ask about Blood-Gor, whose face you saw on the warning poster, turn to **261**.

If you enter the tavern, turn to **233**.

Blood sprays into the air once more, as you hack into your enemy.

Roll one dice to see if luck is on your side.

If you roll a three or less, turn to **379**.

If you roll a four or higher, turn to **364**.

Your arrow thuds into the Snake's soft underbelly. (Remove it from your inventory.) Your enemy hisses and thrashes, before sliding towards you across the stone floor.

If you unleash a second arrow, turn to **256**.

If you draw your sword, turn to **290**.

The woman suddenly hunches her broad shoulders, closes her eyes, and pushes with a huge surge of effort. The veins in the man's arm begin to protrude, his muscles start to spasm, and his expression becomes desperate and etched with pain. Sweat begins to form on both their foreheads, then the man's arm suddenly buckles and slams down onto the table, cracking the rickety wooden legs beneath it.

Berty rises up like a monstrous bear, shaking her fists and roaring with victory.

You have lost the money that you gambled. Reduce your **Crimson Coins** accordingly.

The contest is over, and the table is in ruins, so the crowd begin to disperse into the various lanes that lead from the courtyard. As they do so, you overhear two men talking about Port Acura. The duo leave down a side turning called Dead Man's Walk, but they have disappeared by the time you get there.

If you explore the turning, turn to **286**.

If you leave via a different lane, and follow the signs towards the harbour, turn to **204**.

274

You dash to the center of the ship. Here you are safer, as you are less likely to be knocked into the sea. The tentacle sweeps after you, but more crew members run to your side. They thrust their weapons into the thrashing menace, then you leap forward and deliver a massive sword strike. The tentacle spasms, crashes onto the deck, then slides over the edge.

Glancing around, you see that the other slithering arms are also retreating into the waves. A cry of relief goes up from the men, but it is misguided. The WindRunner suddenly shudders and groans, as if something beneath the water is trying to overturn it. The boat leans dramatically to starboard, and you lose your footing and slide down the deck, towards the surging ocean.

Screams rise up all around you, overpowering the sound of the storm.

Do you possess the special ability of **Scale**?

If so, turn to **258**.

If not, turn to **287**.

275

To your surprise, you suddenly hear a loud squawking, then you find yourself assailed by flapping wings and sharp claws. You are being attacked from above by a large, jet black Parrot. It is Blood-Gor's enraged pet, and it has swooped out of the enemy ship to get revenge for the death of its master.

You attempt to frighten it away, but it merely soars out of reach, then swoops back towards you. It is determined to tear your eyes out with it's ferocious beak, so you will have to fight it to the death!

CAPTAIN'S PET

LIFE FORCE 4   STRIKING SPEED 10

Focus	Move	Damage
1	**Raking Talons**	1
2-3	**Slashing Talons**	1
4-5	**Tearing Beak**	1
6	**Savage Eye Gouge**	2

If you win, turn to **44**.

276

You swerve to the right and narrowly avoid the attack, then you shove the man backwards into the throng. You surge left towards the door, almost tripping over two wrestlers who are rolling about on the floor. All the men in the tavern seem to be having great fun, and they are in no mood to stop fighting. You are nearly at the exit when someone staggers into you. You push him away, but he grabs you and pulls you back. You turn and kick him to the floor, then you see a large figure rushing at you with a piece of timber.

If you duck, turn to **219**.

If you throw a punch at the man's jaw, before he has time to strike, turn to **246.**

277

You edge forward, deeper into the gloom, but you soon come to another heap of rubble which is blocking your route. Looking closer, you notice a blue object amidst the wreckage. (If you wish to take it, add the **Tarnished Gem** to your possessions.)

There is no way onwards, and the water is rising due to the obstruction. Fearing that you might drown, you retrace your steps and climb back up the ladder. Turn to **229**.

278

You see the shaft soaring towards the Giant's head, but the monster quickly raises its arm in defence. The arrow thuds into its bicep, burying itself in the thick muscle. With a snarl, the beast tears it free and crushes it into dust with its massive hand. (Remove one **Arrow** from your inventory.) Before you can make your next move, the Giant pulls a tree from the earth and hurls it across the clearing towards you.

If you leap backwards and jump over it as it crashes and rolls towards you, turn to **295**.

If you leap forward and try to duck under it before it hits the ground, turn to **257**.

279

"How much are you willing to bet?" asks the hunched little creature, whilst holding out the palm of his hand. "Fortune favours the bold," he says, staring at you with an unpleasant, narrow-eyed grin.

If you have changed your mind, and no longer wish to bet, turn to **238**.

Otherwise, you can place one, two, or three coins into his palm. Make your decision now and note down how much money you have given him, then turn to **293**.

280

You skip to the last page, to see if the Captain's notes can shed any light on the mystery of this ill-fated vessel. This is what you read:

The wind has grown weak, and we have barely made way for several days.
A great fog has rolled in over the water, and little can be seen beyond the bow.
Twice in the last hour, the lookout in the crow's nest has spoken of a huge ship, drifting in the mist some way behind us. I have looked, but not seen it for myself.
He seems convinced that we are being followed.

You put the book onto the desk, next to a crimson stained sea chart. Looking at the lines that have been plotted on the paper, you gather that the ship was sailing from Port Acura to Port Kattaran when it ran into trouble.

You pull the handle on the desk's drawer, but it will not open.

If you have **Picklock** and wish to use it, turn to **67**.
If not, turn to **371**.

281

The arrow flies upwards and thuds into the monster's chest. (Remove it from your inventory.) The Giant suddenly storms towards you, roaring with fury whilst trying to crush you under its feet. You dodge its rampaging attack, but the monster kicks the bow from your hand and sends it flying across the clearing.

Turn to **49** to finish the fight with your sword, but reduce your enemy's **Life force** by four points due to the damage caused by your arrows. You can regain your bow at the end of the battle.

282

As you move away from the contraption, you see that the captive is now grinning hideously.

"Long live the Pirates. Long live the curse of the Black Ship!" he shrieks in a cruel voice, then he hurls a leg bone at you, which he must have found in the bottom of his cage.

It whooshes towards your head.

Roll one dice.

If you roll a one, it strikes your temple, drawing blood: reduce your **Life Force** by one point.

If you roll a two or higher, the bone misses you, nearly striking Pelanthius, then it clatters harmlessly to the floor.

You hurry into the next lane, with the criminal's mad laughter echoing after you.

Turn to **204**.

Your arrow thuds into Kazal's chest. (Remove it from your inventory.) Your enemy barely seems to notice, and he charges straight into you, knocking you backwards onto the floor. You roll to your feet, then duck as a huge fist swings close to your head. His eyes are blazing with madness and fury.

(You are now locked in close combat: return to page **350** and conclude the fight with your sword, but reduce your opponent's **Life Force** immediately by two points due to the damage caused by your arrow.)

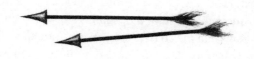

284

THE DREADED CAPTAIN BLOOD-GOR

LIFE FORCE 9   STRIKING SPEED 10

Focus	Move	Damage
1	Wild Kick	1
2-3	Cat O' Nine Tails	2
4-5	Slashing Scimitar	2
6	Brutal Sword Strike	3

If you defeat this dangerous adversary, turn to **252**.

285

You land and duck behind the trees that ring the clearing, then you watch as the dark mass passes overhead. Their eyes burn with faint red lights and their vast numbers smother the glow of the moon. After a few minutes, the swarm has disappeared from view. With a sigh of relief, you climb a tree to ensure the danger has passed. From the high branches, you see that the birds have moved far into the south, so you signal to Pelanthius that the coast is clear. You are about to climb down when you hear the pounding of huge footfalls. Suddenly, the nearby trees begin to shake and rustle, then you see a huge, hulking form barging through the forest towards you.

"A Moon Giant!" cries Pelanthius. "Those things are immune to magic! Quickly, defend yourself!"

Suddenly, the tree you are in is knocked over and you crash to the ground amidst a mess of broken branches and swirling leaves. You have landed in the centre of the clearing and above you looms the Giant. Its face is a jumbled nightmare of twisted features. Its bald head has several pointed ears, and four eyes are dotted above its hideous, fanged mouth. A mystical blue glow surrounds it, making the creature an ominous sight indeed. Pelanthius quickly fires a blast of energy from the tip of his staff, but the spell bounces harmlessly off of the creature's aura. With a growl, the monster swings a clawed hand and the impact hurls the Wizard across the clearing.

You scramble to your feet.

If you have a **Bow** and wish to use it, turn to **250**.

If you leap forward, brandishing your sword, turn to **49**.

286

You soon come to a stagnant stream that cuts through the town. Leaning, crooked dwellings are crammed against the banks, and the water is putrid and clogged with junk. You make your way across the rickety crossing, then you continue down the narrowing lane. Many a foul murder has occurred in Dead Man's Walk, but with your fierce sword close to hand, and the Wizard's staff lighting the way, no one comes to trouble you. You eventually arrive at another junction.

You are wondering which way to go, then you hear distant chatter echoing in the lane to your right. You recognise the voices as those you heard earlier, so you follow the sounds. Turn to **270**.

As you tumble down the deck, your head strikes something hard and blunt, then pain rushes through your skull.

(Reduce your **Life Force** by two points.)

If you are still alive, you spot a sailor clinging to a piece of rope. He grabs you by the arm as you roll past, saving you from a watery grave. All across the ship, the sailors are grabbing hold of anything they can, to stop themselves from plunging into the sea. The situation is becoming more desperate by the second, as the ship is continuing to lean at an ever increasing angle. You look down and see a monstrous mouth emerging from the black ocean. Huge teeth come into view, a gaping vortex of a max, and countless, unblinking eyes.

Suddenly, Pelanthius's head appears through the hatchway behind you, looking shocked and ruffled. A beam of light instantly erupts from his staff and arches downwards. It strikes the head of the beast, and the monster falls silent, ceasing its attack. The Wizard's magic has not wounded it; instead, the spell has put it to sleep. The mega beast drifts down into the depths of the sea, then the WindRunner rights itself and surges loose from the deadly embrace.

Turn to **268**.

A short, stocky little thug, no more than four feet tall, suddenly springs onto your back, trying to bite you with his rotten teeth. You grab him by the shoulders and throw him onto the deck in front of you. He springs up with a wild laugh, and you assume by his expression that he is completely insane. He seems to have lost all of his weapons during the course of the battle, but that does not stop him from charging at you again. Compared to Blood-Gor, this fellow should be less of a challenge, but he is still a dangerous maniac.

DAYNOR, THE MAD DECKHAND

LIFE FORCE 6   STRIKING SPEED 8

Focus	Move	Damage
1	Gut Punch	1
2-3	Arm Chomp	1
4-5	Gnashing Rage	2
6	Deranged Frenzy	2

If you win, turn to **44**.

289

"How lucky are ya feeling?" asks the little creature, whilst holding out the blue palm of his hand. "Fortune favours the bold, so they say."

You can place one, two, or three **Crimson Coins** into his palm. Make your decision now and note down how much you have given him, then turn to **273**.

290

You unsheathe your blade just in time to fend off the lunging jaws! (Finish the fight as normal, but reduce the Snake's **Life Force** immediately by two points, due to the damage caused by your ranged weapon.)

MUTANT SNAKE

LIFE FORCE   14   STRIKING SPEED   8

Focus	Move	Damage
1	Darting Jaws	2
2-3	Spitting Acid	2
4-5	Striking Fangs	3
6	Bone Crushing Grasp	4

If you win, turn to **197**.

You sprint to the edge and drag the sailor back onto the deck. As you do so, you glance around and see the tentacle surging towards you. Your comrade has been badly wounded and he sags onto the floor, bleeding from his forehead. "Leave me," he stutters. "Get away from the edge. Lure it to midships!"

If you ignore him and stand your ground, turn to **218**.

If you follow his advice, turn to **274**.

With a heave, you lift the iron grate in the cobbled floor. A rusty ladder descends into a black tunnel, so you scramble down into the darkness. At the bottom, you find yourself standing knee-deep in sludgy, dark water. The sewerage is flowing westward, as you had expected, and if you follow the current you might well escape the town. However, you have barely started moving when you hear an unnerving clattering in the darkness ahead. Turn to **60**.

As you hand over your money, the woman suddenly hunches her broad shoulders, closes her eyes, and pushes with a huge surge of effort. The veins in the man's arm begin to protrude, his muscles start to spasm, and his expression becomes desperate and etched with pain. Sweat begins to form on his forehead, then his arm suddenly buckles and slams down onto the table, cracking the rickety wooden legs beneath it.

Berty rises up like a monstrous bear, shaking her fists and roaring with victory. You turn to collect your winnings.

If you bet one coin, turn to **329**.

If you bet two, turn to **104**.

If you bet three, turn to **314**.

The lane soon bends, then you spot three men in armour who are members of the City Guard. They are standing by a doorway, talking quietly amongst themselves.

If you speak to them, turn to **337**.

If you walk on, turn to **357**.

You successfully dodge the trunk, which rolls and crashes into the trees at the back of the clearing.

If you quickly loose a second arrow, turn to **281**.

If you draw your sword and rush at your enemy, turn to **269**.

Lightning flashes over the deck as you draw back the bow string. Your arrow flies free and thuds into the Sea Beast's glistening, leathery flesh. Green, corrosive blood splashes down, hissing against the wood. But the tentacle continues forward, seemingly unaware of the wound. You watch as it curls around the sturdy mast!

(Remove one **Arrow** from your belongings.)

To release another arrow, turn to **254**.

If you spring forward and attack it with your sword, turn to **271**.

You kneel on the dank floor and scrutinize the markings. They are mystical symbols, each one surrounded by a white circle. You are no expert in the art of dark magic, but you gather that the fortune teller was trying to enact some kind of sinister ritual, in her doomed pursuit of eternal youth.

If you have not yet done so, you may examine:

The trinkets, turn to **39**.

Or the bowls, turn to **227**.

If you are ready to leave, turn to **129**.

You make your way through the lanes, and it is not long before you see an ale soaked tavern, nestled in a narrow side street. A sign above the door reads: *The Black Anchor*.

If you tell the Wizard to ask around at the harbour, whilst you make inquiries at the tavern, turn to **209**.

If you decide to stay together, and press on towards the docks, turn to **133**.

299

A tall man, wearing a necklace of human ears, is charging towards you. He is the ship's cook, and he has a collection of knives in his belt. They are the tools with which he kills his enemies and prepares his food. He was too eager to join the battle to remain in the galley.

RIKAM, THE SHIP'S COOK

LIFE FORCE 8   STRIKING SPEED 9

Focus	Move	Damage
1	Elbow to the Skull	1
2-3	Knife Throw	2
4-5	Slashing Blade	2
6	Devious Strike	2

If you win, turn to **44**.

Illustration Opposite

As you approach the end of the path, you see two more ominous trees that resemble baleful faces. Their roots creep down to the edge of the trail, and their leaves are shivering with mystical energy. Eerie yawns drift from the mouth shaped hollows in their trunks, as if they are waking from a deep slumber.

If you have **Haste**, turn to **242**.

If you do not have **Haste**, turn to **231**.

301

As you move toward the desk, you notice that the glittering magic has followed you in, and it is now landing like petals of light on your skin.

Suddenly, your temperature starts to rise, and it feels as though your flesh is burning! You stumble backwards into the garden, writhing as if you were on fire. (Reduce your **Life Force** by two points.)

The cottage door slams shut behind you, then a blast of wind hurls you across the clearing, dumping you by the alley. It would seem that you are no longer welcome here! You clamber to your feet and scurry out of the garden. The glittering magic does not follow you, and the scolding pain immediately vanishes. You decide that it would be unwise to return to the house, so you turn into Lore Street and hurry on your way.

Turn to **198**.

You feel the temperature drop. The landscape seems to envelop you, and you realise that you have somehow passed through the glass, into another place. The mirror was a gateway, and you now find yourself standing at the base of the hill. It is deep in the night; a cold mist drifts at your feet, and dark grassland spreads out in all directions. You are not entirely sure where you are, but you sense that you have travelled very far from the port.

A wolflike creature howls, far away in a twisted wood, then you hear the muttering of female voices up on the hill. Behind you stands another mirror, six feet in height and two in width, much like the last.

If you sneak up the hill, so that you can hear the conversation, turn to **132**.

If you try to step back through the glass, turn to **331**.

You stand near the helm and watch as the men row out and board the vessel. After a short while, the sailors return with grim news. "The ship has been damaged in a battle," they explain, "and she is slowly sinking. The crew are all missing, as is her cargo, and the decks are stained with blood."

"This is the work of Pirates," spits Fornax. "Hopefully those murderers will have moved into others waters, but we should be ready, just in case." He turns to one of his crew. "Make sure the crow's nest is manned day and night. And put lookouts near the bow and stern. Too many eyes are better than too few."

The Sea Star pushes on, leaving the sinking vessel in the arms of the sea.

As the sky grows dark, Fornax hands the helm to a trusted crewman, then you both head below deck to have supper with the sailors. You are presented with a plate of stale bread and slop. It is a lame sight, but it keeps your hunger at bay. The hour has now grown late, so you decide to get some rest. Turn to **84**.

304

As soon as you start to fiddle with the lock, the area grows eerily quiet, then the butterflies stop moving; they sit motionless on the flowers, as if watching you.

Slowly, the sparkling magic drifts up from the grass and begins to twinkle in the air around you.

If you continue to pick the lock, turn to **339**.

If not, turn to **321**.

305

As your enemy slumps to the ground, you turn and see that Valantis has knocked out the other scoundrel with his bare fists. "Well well," says the captain, glancing at you, then the Wizard. "It is good to know that you can handle yourselves in battle. You should fit in well with my crew. Come, let us get to our bunks, I have had enough of Port Kattaran for one night."

You follow him down to the harbour, and soon find yourself standing by the gangplank, which leads up to the ship. Turn to **120**.

Turning towards the shelves, you see that the bowls are filled with embalming fluid. Each one houses a severed hand, which is floating in the liquid. It seems that many an unfortunate visitor has met their end in this house of horrors.

You must now pick an option which you have not yet chosen.

If you investigate the chalk markings on the floor, turn to **240**.

If you examine the stuffed birds, turn to **234**.

If you look at the trinkets, turn to **80**.

If you are ready to leave, turn to **129**.

307

You halt at the first door. A sign by the entrance reads: *Teren's Trading Post*. There is nothing useful to buy here, but you may trade your unwanted items for coins.

If you have a **Small Goblin Statue**
the trader will purchase it for **two Crimson Coins**

If you have a **Small Fairy Statue**
he will buy it for **three Crimson Coins**

For a **Sapphire Ring**
he will give you **four Crimson Coins**

For **Ariana's Necklace**
he will give you **five Crimson Coins**

For a **Black Crystal Necklace**
he will give you **four Crimson Coins**

If you possess a **Tarnished Gem**
he will offer you **two Crimson Coins**

If you sell any of the items, remove them from your Character Sheet and increase your money accordingly. When you have finished, you leave and continue down the lane.

Turn to **244.**

308

You have a sinking feeling that your journey through the mirror has set you on a path to failure. You watch as the riders move away, leaving you in the ruined landscape.

Over the coming days, an ill wind blows in over the sea, and the land is scorched by more burning rain. You are forced to take shelter in the caves by the cliffs, to escape the searing droplets. You wait, hoping that the weather will pass, but each morning the sky only darkens, creating a sense of perpetual night. Days pass, and the rain is endless. However, on the third dawn, you see movement near the remains of Port Kattaran. A family of travellers are fleeing south, and they have created a metal roof over their wagon, to protect themselves from the weather. The protective sheet has started to melt and corrode, so you usher them into the caves. You sit and talk, and you soon learn of a great army of men and Elves which perished in the north, washed away by a terrible shadow. The family stay for only one night. They patch the holes in the roof, then push on south. There is no room for you to join them, so you wait, trapped by the endless, scorching rain. Weeks pass, and the land slowly dies around you. The rain gradually destroys the trees and animals, until no food is left to scavenge.

When the great shadow of Evoka comes out of the north, your enemy has become too powerful to ever defeat, and your body is too weak from hunger to flee.

Had you not stepped through the portal, you may well have stopped Evoka in his tracks, but only doom awaits you now.

Your quest has failed.

309

You are feeling tired, so you sit against a heap of ropes and drift into a shallow slumber. The sound of the waves melt away, and you begin to dream. Through your mind's eye, you see a wild field in a strange land, dappled with the shadows of purple clouds. A woman's voice drifts through the sky, and you sense the presence of a powerful entity. "I have been watching you for many years," says the voice. "Evil awaits you. But I have seen the courage you possess; do not let it falter."

"Who are you?" you mutter.

The voice speaks again, but it is suddenly distant, and you cannot hear the words. A darkness begins to fill your mind, then a cold, claw-like mountain rises up in your subconscious. There is a cavernous entrance near its summit, filled with fiery light, and you feel a powerful wind dragging you towards it...

You wake suddenly, disturbed by a gust of wind, and your face is chilled by the cold spray which is coming up over the deck. You pull your clothes tighter around you, then gaze out over the scene. Turn to **334**.

310

You reach the harbour and peer around. The level of destruction makes the hairs rise on the nape of your neck. To your surprise, there is no sign of Fornax's ship. Instead, five black galleons are present, none of which were here when you last visited the harbour. All the ships are abandoned, their sails torn and their decks smashed. Debris floats in the water around them, and the burning rain has set fire to their sails. As you watch, the lights slowly dim, then go out, as the ships crumble into the sea.

"Pelanthius," you mutter. "Where are you?"

You turn, once more distracted by movement on the hill. No life exists down in the town, so you scramble back across the ruined landscape, to see what moves upon the moonlit rise. Turn to **20**.

311

You read the labelled bottles. Most of the potions are cures for minor ailments, such as the common cold. However, you do find some health potions which are listed below.

(Note: because they are so small, you may drink the **Health Potions** at any time, even during combat. Their effects are instantaneous. When you use a potion, remove it from your inventory.)

A **Tiny Health Potion**
that will add two points to your **Life Force**
(One available) Cost: **one Crimson Coin**

A **Small Health Potion**
that will add five points to your **Life Force**
(One available) Cost: **four Crimson Coins**

Purchase what you want, reduce your money accordingly, then add the items to your Character Sheet.

When you are ready to move on, turn to **333**.

312

The man eventually quietens down, then returns with a jar of moss. He gives it to you proudly, and you mumble a thank you.

(Add the **Jar of Pink Moss** to your belongings, if you want to keep it.)

He opens his mouth to speak, then his eyes become vacant, and he stands motionless with a slack jaw, as if he has drifted into a daydream.

If you clamber over the hilltop and continue down the lane, turn to **201**.

If you wait, turn to **46**.

The translucent figures tear into you and rip the beating heart from your body.

Your hopes for a successful adventure have been brought to a sudden end.

314

The creature suddenly turns and dashes through the crowd, trying to escape with your money. Several men reach out to grab him, but he weaves past them and takes flight into a nearby lane.

If you give chase, turn to **394**.

If you let him go, turn to **362**.

315

The Earthworm collapses in a mess of splintered bones. Twisting in the saddle, you suddenly realise that Pelanthius is nowhere to be seen. You can see his horse, standing amidst the chaos, but the saddle is empty. As you scan the crowd in the hope of seeing him, you are distracted by a huge Skeleton which is standing thirty feet away. It is twice the height of anything else on the battlefield. It has four arms, and in each hand it grips a long spear of sharpened bone. It suddenly hurls three spears towards you, and the force with which they are thrown is immense.

You must act swiftly to avoid being impaled!

If you still possess your **Amossan Shield**, turn to **23**.

If not, turn to **154**.

316

The serpent turns and lunges at you with its dripping fangs. At such close range, the attack is impossible to dodge. You cry out in pain as its jaws sink into your skin! Reduce your **Life Force** by two points, then, if you are still alive, turn to **153**.

317

A crimson stained sea chart lies on the oak tabletop. Looking at the lines that have been plotted on the paper, you gather that the ship was sailing from Port Acura to Port Kattaran when it ran into trouble.

You pull on the drawer, but it is locked.

If you have **Picklock** and wish to open it, turn to **207**.

If not, turn to **332**.

You manage to free one of your hands and strike out with your weapon, smashing through its shoulder. You have destroyed one of its arms, but you are unable to stop your enemy from breathing a blast of fire from its glowing jaws. You are scolded by the heat, which causes you to cry out in agony.

Reduce your **Life Force** by three points, then, if you are still alive, turn to **134**.

Pelanthius's voice echoes into your mind. "Stay with me!" he says. "Do not leave my side!"

Streams of dark energy suddenly erupt from Evoka's hands, turning hundreds of Elves to dust. Pelanthius raises his staff in alarm, and a sphere of light appears around the remaining army, holding back the rays of death. Six hundred warriors remain, still surging towards the monstrous figure, eight hundred metres between them and closing fast. The darkness continues to flow from Evoka's hands, bouncing off of the white sphere, and you see Pelanthius start to tremble from the effort, as he continues to deflect Evoka's attacks.

You thunder alongside the Wizard, just feet away from him, but your flesh is now starting to decay. You have entered the zone of Evoka's deadly aura, and it is sucking the life from you! Your body begins to wither and the strength starts to ebb from your muscles.

(Reduce your **Life Force** by ten points!)

If you survive, turn to **347**.

Illustration Opposite

Your opponent's clothes rip as his body swells and expands. His skin suddenly turns hard and scaly, then his tongue splits in half at the end. In a few seconds, Kazal has transformed into a Giant Snake, with a body as thick as a tree trunk. The staircase groans and cracks, then you leap backwards as the whole thing collapses under the weight of the colossal serpent. You retreat to the back of the room, hovering near Pelanthius in order to protect him.

If you have a **Bow** and want to fire at your enemy, turn to **272**.

If you do not have a **Bow**, or if you choose not to use it, you must defend yourself with your sword.

MUTANT SNAKE

LIFE FORCE 14   STRIKING SPEED 8

Focus	Move	Damage
1	Darting Jaws	2
2-3	Spitting Acid	2
4-5	Striking Fangs	3
6	Bone Crushing Grasp	4

If you defeat your serpentine enemy, turn to **197**.

321

The butterflies go about their business once more, and the magic begins to seep into your muscles, rejuvenating your senses. A feeling of wellbeing enters your mind. (Increase your **Life Force** by two points.)

You stand still for a short while, consumed by a sense of peace, then the butterflies flitter away, up into the evening sky. There is nothing more for you to do here, so you make your way back down the alley and onto Lore Street. Turn to **198**.

322

You tell Fornax that you will return later, then he nods and heads up onto the deck. You walk into the narrow alley and up to the black door. As you stand before the entrance, the sounds from the harbour fade away and a deep silence settles over you. Just as you are about to knock, the door creaks open by itself and a quiet voice invites you in.

Turn to **188**.

323

You slowly lift the goblet. It is weightier than you expected, and strange, ghastly etchings have been carved into its surface. You warily part your lips, but you take only a sip before hurling the cup against the wall. Thick, dark blood spills out, staining the floor, and you grimace with disgust.

However, a moment later, you feel your skin tightening around your eyes. You glimpse yourself in the mirror. You are unsure if it is your imagination, but your appearance has become slightly more youthful.

(Increase your **Life Force** by two points.)

Turn to **345**.

You suddenly feel compelled to duck, and you just avoid the crack of a bat as it sweeps over your head!

You whirl around and see two crewmen; one wearing brutish knuckle-dusters, the other carrying a club. "Give us ya money," the taller man snarls. "Or we're gonna beat ya into a pulp."

You refuse to cower, so you draw your sword in a flash of defiance. The shorter man suddenly swings his fist towards your head, but you dodge the blow and slam your sword pommel into his jaw. Several of his teeth are smashed from his mouth, then he crumples to the floorboards in an unconscious state. As he hits the ground, the man with the club surges forward, trying to crack your skull with his weapon. Despite his heavy build, his attacks are fast, and you realise that he is a fighter of considerable skill. You have no choice but to defend yourself.

STOCKY THUG

LIFE FORCE 8   STRIKING SPEED 9

Focus	Move	Damage
1	**Brutish Headbutt**	1
2-3	**Club to the Ribs**	1
4-5	**Club to the Face**	2
6	**Club to the Skull**	2

If you win, turn to **199**.

You leave the shop and make your way back down the street. However, you have not gone far when something stops you in your tracks. There is a very narrow alley to your left, which you failed to notice earlier. As you approach it, you see a sign on the wall which reads:

This way to the home of Leanor the Healer.

If you explore the turning, turn to **178**.
If you walk past it, turn to **198**.

326

A spinning blade suddenly flies through the chaos, narrowly missing your throat.

Before you can turn to see who threw it, another whooshes towards your ribs, forcing you to deflect it with your sword.

If you spin to the left, to see who is throwing the blades, turn to **299**.

If you dodge to the right, and push deep into the fray, turn to **211**.

327

Your opponent is an entity of immeasurable power, and you do not yet have the knowledge to defeat him.

You curse beneath your breath, but a plan quickly forms in your mind: the skeletal ranks have thinned, and you recall seeing a large war horse tethered nearby. If you galloped out of the main gate, and smashed your way onto the easterly road, you could then lure the maniac away from the town.

It is an insanely dangerous plan, but if you think it might work, turn to **11**.

Otherwise, you will have to challenge your enemy to a fight, one against one, turn to **22**.

328

The Amossans fought bravely but, in the end, the enemy's vast numbers proved too much for them. Had your choices been different, maybe you could have saved them, but victory is not reserved for you this day.

You are overwhelmed by the skeletal army and the world is Evoka's for the taking.

329

The creature returns the coin that you gave him, then he hands you another. (Adjust your money accordingly.)

"I'm glad you didn't bet more," he mutters.

The contest is now over, the table is in ruins, and the crowd begin to disperse into the various lanes that lead from the courtyard. As they do so, you overhear two men discussing Port Acura.

They leave down a side turning called Dead Man's Walk, but they have disappeared by the time you get there.

If you explore the turning, turn to **286**.

If you leave via a different lane, and follow the signs towards the harbour, turn to **204**.

330

Torayus suddenly grabs you, sinking his teeth into your neck.

(Reduce your **Life Force** by three points!)

If you are still alive, you break free and smash him in the face with the pommel of your sword, knocking him backwards. But there is no look of pain on your enemy's face. His white eyes are now glowing; the mark, where you struck him with your pommel, vanishes, and a wide grin appears across his silent, bloodstained mouth. He stalks towards you once again, ready for battle.

Return to **211** to continue the fight, but if you have dealt any damage to Torayus, his wounds have fully healed and his **Life Force** has returned to ten.

331

You step towards the mirror, hoping that you might somehow pass back into the fortune teller's house, but you do not. Your reflection stares back at you, and your fingers touch the cold, smooth glass.

Turn to **132**.

332

You pick up the ship's log and skip to the last entry, to see if the Captain's notes can shed any light on the mystery of this ill-fated vessel. This is what you read:

The wind has grown weak, and we have
barely made way for several days.
A great fog has rolled in over the water,
and little can be seen beyond the bow.
Twice in the last hour, the lookout in the
crow's nest has spoken of a huge ship,
drifting in the mist some way behind us.
I have looked, but not seen it for myself.
He seems convinced that we are being followed.

Pondering the words, you place the book onto the desk. Turn to **371**.

333

You step back into the deepening night.

If you continue down the lane, turn to **142**.

If you are ready to rejoin Pelanthius, and move on towards the palace, turn to **103**.

The sun is slowly sinking towards the horizon, casting its glow onto the crests of the waves. As the sky reddens, you hear a call from a man in the crow's nest. Gazing east, you see another trading vessel, drifting with lowered sails and no visible crew.

(Make a note on your Character Sheet that you have encountered an **abandoned vessel**.)

"That ship is called The Silver Shoal," mutters a sailor, who is standing nearby. "It went missing some time ago."

Fornax calls upon a small group of sailors to investigate.

If you volunteer to join them, turn to **255**.

If you remain on The Sea Star, turn to **303**.

As you approach the split in the tunnel, beams of burning light suddenly stream out of the skull's eyes. You are struck by the searing heat, and you stagger backwards, your voice echoing with agony.

(Reduce your **Life Force** by three points!)

You hear an eerie sound, like insane laughter, rattling in the gloom, then the skull suddenly explodes in a ball of magical energy.

Huge cracks appear in the walls, then the ceiling tumbles down into the water around you, almost crushing you! You manage to stumble backwards and escape the deluge, but after the dust has settled, you see that the way ahead has been completely blocked by rubble. You cannot escape via the tunnels after all: the evil that has beset this town will not allow it!

You return to the ladder and climb back up the grimy rungs. Turn to **229**.

As you scramble down the slope, you look back and see the man standing at the summit. He is shaking his fist at you, whilst shouting in a psychotic manner. Suddenly, countless rats swarm out of the debris near his feet and chase you down the hill. Several rodents clamber onto Pelanthius's robes, whilst others stab their teeth into your legs.

(Reduce your **Life Force** by one point.)

If you are still alive, you batter them away and escape down the lane. Turn to **201**.

"Welcome to Amossa," says one of the men, as you walk towards him. "You do not look like you come from these parts."

You explain that you came in on a merchant ship and are looking for goods to buy.

"You picked a bad time to visit these shores," he responds. "An army of bones gathers at our borders, whilst the King sits quietly upon his throne."

"I am gravely aware of these facts," you mutter, "but with some luck, your misfortunes will not persist." You scan your surroundings. "I am looking for items that might be of use to a warrior."

"If you want adventuring equipment, you should explore this shop," he says, pointing to the doorway behind him. "The prices are reasonable."

You take his advice and step inside.

(Note: below are the items that gain your attention. Because it is so small, you may drink the **Health Potion** at any time, even during combat. When you use a potion, remove it from your Character Sheet.)

A Tiny Health Potion that will add two points
to your **Life Force** (One available)
Cost: **two Crimson Coins**

Spiked Climbing Boots
(One pair available) Cost: **three Crimson Coins**

When you are done, turn to **361**.

You clamber into your bunk and fall asleep almost instantly. When you wake, six hours later, you find that the ship is already underway. You head up onto the deck and see Fornax standing at the wheel. Port Kattaran is slowly sinking into the distance, and there is soon nothing but water all around.

"How long will it take to reach Port Acura?" You ask.

"If the wind remains good, I should hope to get there by tomorrow night," he answers.

"What of the other vessel that was docked beside us, The WindRunner?" you ask. "I thought it was also due to set sail for Acura this morning?"

"We left before it," says Fornax.

You sense that Fornax is not a fan of idle conversation, so you sit on the deck's edge and remain there for the rest of the day. Huge, black dolphins follow the ship for several hours, leaping through the waves and around the bow, but as evening draws in, they vanish from view. You realise that you have not seen Pelanthius all day, and you presume that he is reading or snoozing in his room, such is the way of Wizards.

The ship presses onwards, into the great ocean.

Roll one dice to see what random events the evening has in store for you.

If you roll a four or less, turn to **334**.

If you roll a five or a six, turn to **309**.

You push open the entrance and peer into the dwelling. There is a single, circular room within, with a bed against one wall, a table in the middle, and a chair by a fireplace. Gold and red light filters in through a stained glass window, and you can see that no one has been here for days.

If you head inside to look at the notes, which have been left on the table, turn to **301**.

If you are beginning to feel bad about this intrusion, you may close the door and return to Lore Street, turn to **198**.

340

"I am looking for my container of pink moss," he mutters. "I need it for my next batch of potions, but it seems to be missing." He is distracted by his dilemma, and he continues to search the drawers without turning to look at you.

If you have a jar of **Pink Moss**, which you would like to sell, turn to **214**.

If not, you scan the shelves whilst he goes about his business, turn to **311**.

341

For three days you make your way across the landscape. Always the sky remains dark, swathed in endless clouds which darken the further north you go. On a cold morning, between a mountain range and the ocean, you see a large force gathered on the plains: two thousand humans and Elves, all on horseback. Never have you seen such an army, and your travelling companions seem briefly to lose their fears. You ride through the vast ranks, until at length you spy a pointed hat among the many helms, then you gallop forward to Pelanthius's side and tell him of your adventures since you parted.

"By the Gods," says the Wizard, as you both dismount, "I did not know whether I would see you again." He hugs you, then steps back, gripping your shoulders. A smile stretches across his face, yet his eyes are sad at the same time. "Dark days are upon us, my friend," he says. "After you disappeared, I searched Port Kattaran and found WrettleNeck's house. I deduced what had happened to you, but the mirror would not let me pass through it. I set off on my own to trap Evoka in the Underworld, but I failed in my mission." The Wizard shakes his head sorrowfully. "Evoka is moving towards us. He has sensed our presence. This will be our last stand."

"Can we stop him?" you ask.

The Wizard's eyes merely shimmer with restrained grief, and he does not answer.

Across the great plain, a wind suddenly begins to blow, carrying a sickness upon the air.

"He is coming," says Pelanthius, in a quiet tone. "Stay close to me, my friend. Death has come for us, but let us not cower in fear. If nothing else, we will make this evil regret the day it set eyes upon us."

He springs into his saddle - looking sterner than you have ever seen him - then he gazes to where the sky is darkest. As you clamber onto the horse beside him, you see a murky fog slowly moving across the land, with a huge, lone figure in its depths. Darkness trails from Evoka's shoulders like a cloak of black smoke, which rises up into the sky, forming clouds that move ahead of him. He is far larger than he was when you first saw him from the walls of Mosal; he is almost sixty feet in height, a shimmering silhouette, filled with shifting faces and many arms of drifting smog. With every step, he seems to grow taller. The grass dies around his feet, as if the World's Spirit is being sucked from the ground, up into his body, and you watch as he kills the earth with every ground shaking footfall.

Men begin to tremble in the front row, unable to hide their fear.

Evoka halts and scans the army from a distance. For a moment he is silent, then his loud, terrible laugh shakes the ground, cracking the earth.

"Stay close to me!" says Pelanthius. "It is time to end this... one way or another." He calls out to his steed, then his horse suddenly surges forward, and the whole army follows. Not one person falters, not even the fearful, and never have you heard the thunderous noise of so many hooves. The battle roar of the brave warriors fills your ears, and you grip your sword, your expression stoic and fierce.

Suddenly, Evoka waves his arm, then the ground tears apart in front of you. Your horse leaps the gap, as does Pelanthius's, but hundreds of others go down into the blackness, vanishing into the widening fissure.

"Keep going," shouts Pelanthius, to those who made it. "I have a plan, but we must get close to him!"

They thunder forward, over a thousand horsemen remaining, and the gap between the army and Evoka begins to close. Your enemy opens his mouth and speaks to you, but his voice is so loud that you are almost deafened by the sound! The world seems to shake and tremble at the boom of his words, and his curse suddenly wracks your mind with agony!

(Reduce your **Life Force** by seven points!)

If you are still alive, turn to **319**.

342

The big brute grunts with pain, but he is too sturdy to be injured by an assault to the ribs; in fact he seems to enjoy it! He retaliates by swinging his elbow into the side of your head. (Reduce your **Life Force** by two points.) You are not sure whether his move was entirely by the rules, but you have no time to argue. You stagger sideways towards the edge of the platform, then the crowd cheers as you regain your footing.

Turn to **194**.

343

You gaze at the many flowers that fill the area. The butterflies seem intrigued by your presence, and they land on your arms and on the grass nearby, resting alongside you. The glittering magic slowly seeps into your muscles, rejuvenating your senses, and a feeling of wellbeing enters your mind.

(Increase your **Life Force** by two points.)

You cannot afford to stay here for long, so you climb to your feet. Feeling calm and rested, you make your way down the alley and back onto Lore Street.

Turn to **198**.

344

All the shops in the Merchant's Quarter are now shut and their candles have been extinguished. You make your way back down the lane to meet Pelanthius, then you press on towards the palace.

Turn to **103**.

You step forward and stare at your reflection, then the glass fades to black. You see a strange vision appearing in its depths; a dark landscape with a lonely hill and a crooked tree, bathed in the glow of a sickly moon. A group of huddled women move on the slope; distant shapes silhouetted against a wild and eerie backdrop.

If you continue to watch, turn to **302**.

If not, turn to **228**.

346

You walk on and soon come to the next shop. It belongs to an Alchemist, and you can hear the bubble and pop of chemicals within.

If you enter, turn to **108**.

If you walk on, turn to **142**.

347

One hundred metres remaining, and you now have to crane your neck to look up at the colossus. Suddenly, Pelanthius's expression changes. Never have you seen such rage! Your blood runs cold and your soul shivers with emotion! The Wizard's staff lights up with a huge surge of energy, then he drops the protective sphere. In the next instant, you are dazzled by a huge blast of light. A white beam of energy flies upwards, disrupting Evoka's attacks by coiling around him like a whip of lightning. The God's mouth opens in agony, then he steps backwards with a look of horror, crying out to the black sky. As you watch, the magical beam tightens like a garrotte, severing all of his arms, before tearing into his shadowy form. For a moment, you sense hope from the riders around you. But Evoka has grown too mighty to be defeated, even by such powerful magic. The God somehow bursts free of the burning, magical light, and where his arms were destroyed, more instantly grow back in their place! Evoka's roar rolls like a wave across the land, then he steps forward, trying to crush the steeds beneath his colossal feet. The riders weave around him, striking at his legs with their swords, but from Evoka's savage eyes, streams of dark energy suddenly tear down into the crowd. All of the power that Pelanthius could muster was extinguished by his last spell. Without the protection of the Wizard's sphere, the riders suddenly turn to dust on the wind. No one is spared. Neither Pelanthius, nor you.

When you passed through the mirror, all hope crumbled into oblivion. The world is now chained to a terrible fate, but it is a fate that you will no longer be cursed to witness.

348

Glancing to your left, you see a broad shouldered thug bowling towards you. He has three arms, four eyes, and a bald head covered in scars. He is a mutant: Blood-Gor's second in command. He carries no swords, but his fists are encased in spiked metal gauntlets.

GLUG, THE QUARTERMASTER

LIFE FORCE 8   STRIKING SPEED 9

Focus	Move	Damage
1	Swift Headbutt	1
2-3	Punch to the Gut	2
4-5	Punch to the Ribs	2
6	Punch to the Face	3

If you win, turn to **44**.

349

As you come to the last set of stairs, you are surprised to find rubble blocking your way. You pick your way through it, up into the open, then your blood runs cold. You are standing under the sky, surrounded by ruined buildings that have been almost totally destroyed. Rubble is everywhere and bodies lay strewn amongst the mess. It is night, and no movement can be seen in the ruined landscape. The world is colder, as if the seasons have suddenly changed, and winter feels far deeper than it did when you first entered the dwelling. Droplets of rain fall from the sky, glowing like lava, and they hiss on the ground, corroding the landscape. You dodge beneath an overhang – the remnants of a wrecked building – and wait for the rain to halt, then you re-emerge into the grisly scene. Your heart begins to sink further, and your thoughts darken with encroaching horror. To the east, towards the sea and the coast, fires are burning. To the west, on the hills that overlook what remains of Port Kattaran, you can see movement.

If you stumble east through the wreckage, back to the ship, turn to **310**.

If you move west, towards the hills, turn to **20**.

Illustration Opposite

Kazal's clothes rip at the seams as his arms swell in size. His back hunches, his brow thickens, and in an instant he has almost doubled in height. The potion has transformed him into a monstrous humanoid, with enormous shoulders and gigantic, muscular forearms. His expanded jaw has made room for huge, pointed teeth, and he is no longer recognisable as the person he was. When he roars, it is the rumbling bellow of a brutish creature. He leaps from the top of the stairs and lands at the bottom, cracking the stone beneath his feet. Kazal's body is flowing with inhuman strength, and his fists are now massive lumps of bone-crushing knuckle.

He rushes forward with a savage snarl.

If you have a **Bow** and want to fire at the approaching brute, turn to **283**.

To conclude the fight with your sword, read on:

MUTANT

| LIFE FORCE | 13 | STRIKING SPEED | 8 |

Focus	Move	Damage
1	**Brutal Head-Butt**	3
2-3	**Fist to the Ribs**	3
4-5	**Fist to the Face**	4
6	**Skull Rattling Punch**	4

If you defeat this brutish powerhouse, turn to **197**.

351

You have made a fatal error. As you turn to escape, a Skeleton suddenly leaps forward and plunges its sword into your exposed back. Rowfur tries to defend you, but he is too late. You collapse to the floor, choking on your own blood. The glittering blade has punctured an organ, and you are unable to drag yourself to your feet. A moment later, Rowfur falls alongside you, his eyes fixed in a cold and lifeless stare. You are losing blood fast, and you no longer possess the strength to grasp your sword. A nightmarish form suddenly looms over you, and you see its blade sweeping down towards your neck. Your head rolls away from your body, then darkness fills your mind.

The defence of Mosal has failed.

352

You are badly burnt: reduce your **Life Force** by four points. If you are still alive, you land safely on the walkway, then you glance back as the other bridge sinks beneath the steaming surface. Turn to **123**.

353

Your move works, and you slice through the Skeleton's bone, sending its arm flying into the crowd. However, the wretched menace leaps forward and buries its teeth into your neck. (Lose two **Life Force**.)

If you are still alive, you quickly free yourself and cleave through your enemy's ribcage, splitting its body in two. It crumples to the ground and ceases to move.

Turn to **363**.

The flavour is strong and refreshing, but it has no effect beyond improving your mood.

"A pleasant drink isn't it," says the bartender. "So, what brings you to our fine town?"

Turn to **87**.

355

As you sprint into the lane, the villain throws a vial onto the ground behind him. It shatters and releases a green cloud which burns your eyes and lungs. The mist drifts away, but your vision is blurring and your chest tightening.

If you continue the chase, turn to **396**.

If you halt and allow him to escape, turn to **383**.

356

You cannot escape your enemy's wrath. As you dash back across the bridge, a black tendril of lightning slams into you with the force of a thousand sword strikes. You are not just slain, your body is obliterated from existence - eradicated from the face of the cosmos - so that not even your dust will be left to litter the world. Turn to **390**.

The lane gradually narrows before opening into a circular courtyard. The area is ringed by an assortment of shops, with a fountain at its centre. Several traders are blowing out the candles in their windows, and you realise that the Merchant's Quarter is starting to close.

You hurry around to see what bargains you can find. Below are the items which catch your attention.

Spiked Climbing Boots
(One pair available) Cost: **three Crimson Coins**

A **Fur Coat**
(One available) Cost: **four Crimson Coins**

Purchase what you want and adjust your money accordingly. When you are done, turn to **344**.

358

You leap from the bridge, springing from a floating barrel and onto a rotting piece of timber. You almost tumble into the water, but you manage to dive forward and crash into the belly of the dinghy. You grab hold of the shocked little creature and hold him up, so that he is dangling in front of you. His expression is one of complete horror, and he quickly hands over his money pouch. (You take back the three coins that you gave to him, plus an additional three in winnings; adjust your Character Sheet accordingly.)

You make him row back to the bridge where the other gamblers have now gathered. They cheer you for your daring manoeuvre, and they grab the little creature and begin to collect their winnings. At your request, they give you directions to the harbour, then you set off towards your destination.

Turn to **204**.

359

It is even darker in the lowest level, and you find yourself standing knee-deep in icy water. Nothing stirs here, except for the glinting eyes of rats. Blood is in the water, and there is still no sign of the crew. You cannot be sure how much longer the ship will remain afloat, as you can hear the trickle of the sea seeping through the damaged wood.

If you wish to leave the vessel, turn to **369**.

If you continue to explore, turn to **397**.

360

As you turn to exit the room, you see that the door is slowly closing behind you. You grab the handle, pull it open, and step back into the night. The old woman scurries to the entrance and her voice rings out down the alley, urging you to return.

You ignore her and make your way up the Sea Star's gangplank.

A deep tiredness has settled upon you, so you decide to get some rest.

Turn to **338**.

As you step back into the night, the shopkeeper locks the door behind you. You continue down the lane, but the Merchant's Quarter is now starting to close, and the traders are extinguishing the candles in their windows.

You return to Pelanthius and press on towards the palace. Turn to **103**.

362

You have more important things to do than chase the little villain around Kattaran, so you leave that job to the other angry gamblers. (If you have not already done so, remove the three **Crimson Coins** from your inventory.) You decide to follow the signs towards the harbour. Turn to **204**.

Swords swish and axes slam with brutal force into the sturdy Amossan shields. Several men fall in the skirmish but, after a few minutes, the final abominations are reduced to a pile of shattered remnants. You quickly scan the battlefield, but not a single opponent remains.

Across the valley, many brave men lie upon the ground, stricken and wounded. You spot Faranen amongst them, slumped against a rock with an expression of pain. His breastplate has been dented by a savage spear strike, but his injuries are not fatal. As you move towards him, you see that Pelanthius is already kneeling at his side. The old Wizard is uninjured, but he looks weary and out of breath.

"The evil in this valley has been crushed," says Faranen, "but I am too wounded to continue. You must go with the Wizard and follow the gorge to the summit of the mountain. Our victory is not secured until the gateway is destroyed!"

A group of men, around forty in total, step forward and offer to help you. The rest are too badly injured to continue.

If you tell Pelanthius to stay and help the wounded, whilst you set off with the warriors, turn to **121**.

If you would rather Pelanthius joined you on the final stage of your quest, turn to **43**.

The tentacle releases the mast and swings towards you, trying to knock you into the sea. You dive onto the floor, narrowly avoiding its attack. Two sailors rush to your aid, stabbing the enemy with boat hooks, but the blood-soaked tentacle sweeps around and knocks them over the side. You briefly hear their screams, then their voices are silenced forever as they plunge into the waves.

With an enraged expression, you leap forward to strike the tentacle again. Turn to **387**.

You have made a fatal error. As soon as the defenders begin to back away from the gate, the Skeletons swarm in through the gaps. The men panic and flee in all directions, but many of them are cut down by a sudden hail of ancient arrows. A chaotic scene erupts, and rather than escaping, you suddenly find yourself surrounded by skeletal forms. You cannot fight a battle on all fronts, and a glittering blade suddenly punctures your back, piercing through to your heart. As you hit the ground, you hear the screams of men and women ringing out over the courtyard. A wretched form looms over you, and a rusty spear suddenly lances towards your head. Darkness consumes your mind, and the cries of the stricken tumble into silence.

The fate of Mosal will be written in blood.

366

You spend a while strolling through the dingy lanes of Port Kattaran. You see several fights and two attempted muggings, but fortunately you are not caught up in the brawls. After finding a coin on the floor, you enter a gambling den and spend an hour betting on rat races. Luck is with you, and you increase your wealth.

(Roll one dice and add that many **Crimson Coins** to your belongings; this is in addition to the coin that you found on the floor.)

Pleased with your winnings, you make your way back to the ship. The hour is now very late, so you decide to get some rest.

Turn to **338**.

367

You search the bodies and find **twelve Crimson Coins**, which is in addition to any money that the Thief stole from you. You also find a **Small Health Potion** which you may drink at any time, even during combat. When consumed, the magical brew will instantly increase your **Life Force** by five points. (Add what you take to your Character Sheet, then read on.).

If you wish to spend some more time exploring the grimy network of alleyways, turn to **106**.

If you would rather leave this notorious part of town, turn to **198**.

After surveying the ship, you discover that The WindRunner has been damaged, but is still seaworthy.

Valantis looks relieved. "It seems that luck has not abandoned us completely," he says. "I shall return to the helm and get us to Acura as swiftly as possible."

The rain soon passes, but a blustery wind continues to fill the sails. Dawn comes, painting the sky in purple shades, and you stand on the deck with your hand on the hilt of your sword. Come evening, you head downstairs and eat alongside the other sailors. There is much talk of your recent heroics, and your plate is stacked high in a sign of gratitude.

(Increase your **Life Force** by two points.)

When you are done, you head back outside. As night draws in, you hear the lookout's voice ringing out from the perch on the mast. "Land ahoy," he bellows. "Land ahoy!"

Pelanthius appears through the hatchway, and you both walk to the bow and peer into the darkness. The lights of Acura begin to glitter in the distance, and you see that the port is nestled in a bay at the foot of the sea cliffs. You slowly sail towards it.

Turn to **118**.

You suddenly hear the bending and snapping of timbers, and a large crack appears in the hull. Before you can escape, water gushes in, knocking you off of your feet. For a brief moment you are surrounded by swirling bubbles, then you burst above the surface and drag yourself out of the hold. You are now on the second level, but the ship is leaning further and further to starboard. You sprint towards the hatchway which leads onto the top deck.

Turn to **380**.

You open the door and step through into a dimly lit room. The walls are covered in tapestries which depict the night sky, and a fat spider watches you from its web near the wall-mounted candle.

A thin old woman sits at a round table in the middle of the room, dressed in red robes. Long grey hair hangs over her shoulders, and her skin is etched with deep wrinkles. You can tell that she might once have been pretty beyond comparison, but the ravages of time stole her beauty long ago. You have an uneasy feeling about this place. A weight of sadness lingers in the air, as if the dwelling is haunted by lost souls.

"Many people have died here," you mutter aloud, without meaning to.

The woman shakes her head. "Your senses deceive you," she says, quietly. "But there is some truth to your words." You feel the air growing colder, and her eyes glitter darkly. "I commune with the Spirit Winds," she says. "It is they who you sense, and whose breathless voices drift in the shadows, for only me to hear."

She lights a black candle in front of her, scatters several cat bones onto the tabletop, then asks for a single crimson coin.

You pause.

"Does your heart yearn to flee, for fear of what it might learn?" she asks.

If you wish to sit at the table, you must first give her a coin; remove it from your inventory, then turn to **215**.

If you make your excuses and leave, turn to **360**.

371

There is nothing else of interest in the captain's quarters.

If you leave the cabin and descend into the hold, turn to **359**.

If you wish to leave the ship, turn to **249**.

You are far too quick for the little villain, and you easily catch up with him. You grab him and lift him up, so that he is dangling in front of you. He now has a terrified expression, and he quickly returns your money. (You take back the coins that you gave him, plus an additional three. Adjust your Character Sheet accordingly.) You release him into the arms of the other gamblers, then you press on towards the harbour.

Turn to **204.**

373

You soon come to a narrow alley on your left, with a rickety shop door at its end. There is no sign by the entrance, but a collection of blue candles are burning on the doorstep.

If you investigate, turn to **392.**

If you walk on, turn to **357.**

If you return to Pelanthius and make your way towards the palace, turn to **103.**

374

Pelanthius catches up with you. "Come," he says. "We cannot be chasing this villain all over Kattaran; we have more important matters at hand. Let us move on to the harbour."

If you have not already done so, remove **three Crimson Coins** from your inventory, then turn to **204**.

375

As you turn to push back through the defenders, a leaping Skeleton suddenly plunges its sword into your exposed back. Rowfur tries to defend you, but he is too late. You collapse to the ground, choking on your own blood. The glittering blade must have punctured an organ, and you are unable to drag yourself to your feet. A moment later, Rowfur falls alongside you, his eyes fixed in a cold and lifeless stare. You are losing blood fast, and you have lost the strength to grasp your sword. A nightmarish form looms over you, and you see the edge of a blade sweeping down towards your neck.

Darkness suddenly cloaks your vision, and the sounds of war tumble into silence.

The defence of Mosal has failed.

376

The drink has some mild healing properties: increase your **Life Force** by one point.

"A good choice," says the bartender. "So, what brings you to our fine town?"

Turn to **87**.

377

Beams of energy suddenly leap from Evoka's eyes, striking your body. You are obliterated from existence, and not even your dust will be left to litter the world.

Turn to **390**.

378

You parry your enemy's strike, then you cleave off its arm and smash through its ribcage, splitting its body in two. It crumples to the ground and ceases to move.

Turn to **363**.

379

The hot liquid splashes onto your arm, burning your flesh. (Reduce your **Life Force** by two points.) If you are still alive, turn to **251** to engage in close combat, but reduce your opponent's **Life Force** immediately by four points, due to your arrow and sword strikes.

You burst into the open and stumble to the edge of the listing ship. Fornax's men have already scrambled back into the longboat, and they are shouting up at you.

"Get off the deck!" they yell. "She's going under!"

You dive into the waves just as the vessel cracks in two. Rough hands drag you into the safety of the longboat, then you look back as the doomed ship sinks beneath the surface. You take a deep breath before rowing back to The Sea Star.

"That was a close call," says Fornax. "What did you find over there?"

"No crew, just blood everywhere," you respond.

"Pirates," he spits. "We had best keep the crow's nest manned day and night. And I will tell the crew to be vigilant. Too many lookouts are better than too few." Fornax pats you on the shoulder, pleased that you made it back alive, then The Sea Star sails onwards.

The stars soon begin to shimmer on the rolling waves, so you head below deck to have supper with the sailors. You are given a bowl of dried food. It has little nutritional value, but at least it suppresses your hunger. The hour has now grown late, so you decide to get some rest. Turn to **84**.

381

You stoop at the last moment and the blades miss you, vanishing like an illusion as they fly past. Turn to **164**.

382

The skeletal ranks have thinned, and you recall seeing a large war horse tethered nearby. If you galloped out of the main gate, and smashed your way onto the easterly road, you could then lure the maniac away from the town.

It is an insanely dangerous plan, but if you think it might work, turn to **11**.

Otherwise, you will have to challenge your enemy to a fight, one against one: turn to **22**.

383

You place your hands over your stinging eyes. The effects of the gas soon wear off and you are none the worse for your ordeal. However, the treacherous scoundrel has escaped. (If you have not already done so, remove **three Crimson Coins** from your inventory.) You decide to press on towards the harbour.

Turn to **204**.

384

Roll one dice to see if luck is on your side. Add two to the result if you possess an **Enchanted, Emerald Bracelet** or a **Glittering Bone Charm**.

If the total is four or higher, turn to **61**.

If the total is three or less, turn to **313**.

You search the body and find **eight Crimson Coins** in the trouser pocket, this is in addition to any money that the Thief stole from you. You also find a **Small Health Potion** which you may drink at any time, even during combat. When consumed, the magical brew will instantly increase your **Life Force** by five points. Add what you want to your Character Sheet, then decide what to do next.

If you wish to spend some more time exploring the grimy network of alleyways, turn to **106**.

If you would rather leave this notorious part of town, turn to **198**.

386

You spring forward and hack into the monstrous form. Acid blood splashes onto the deck, hissing against the wood.

Turn to **251** to engage in close combat, but reduce your opponent's **Life Force** immediately by two points, as you struck first.

Your blade sweeps down, creating another gaping wound. You spring backwards to avoid the spray of corrosive blood, then the tentacle spasms and crashes onto the deck. It slides over the edge and vanishes beneath the waves. As you turn, you see countless more tentacles rising into the night. They suddenly grip the vessel and pull backwards, causing the WindRunner to lean to starboard. With an expression of horror, you lose your footing and slide down the deck, towards the far edge of the ship.

Screams rise up all around you, overpowering the sound of the storm.

Do you possess the special ability of **Scale**?

If so, turn to **258**.

If not, turn to **287**.

You soon come to a filthy river that cuts between the cramped houses. A bridge once spanned the waterway, but it now lies broken. A group of people are in the process of repairing it, so you ask for directions to the harbour. "This crossing was smashed in a recent raid," they tell you, "so you'll have to go over Desecration Hill." They point back the way you came, then they give you some advice. "Keep your eyes out for Mad Morik. He lives in the junk pile and his mood changes like the wind. If you meet him, be polite, but don't hang around if he starts to daydream."

The men return to their work, so you head back to the previous turning. Turn to **266**.

You spend a while strolling through the dingy lanes of Port Kattaran. You see several fights and two attempted muggings, but fortunately you are not caught up in the brawls. After finding a coin on the floor, you enter a gambling den and bet the money on a rat race. Luck is with you, and an hour later you have increased your wealth. (Roll one dice and add that many **Crimson Coins** to your belongings; this is in addition to the coin that you found on the floor.)

Pleased with your winnings, you decide to make your way back to the ship. As you approach the harbour, you once again see the narrow alley with the black door.

If you now wish to visit the Fortune Teller, turn to **370**.

If you are ready to sleep, turn to **338**.

Evoka has kept his word by slaying you. And now that you are dead, he will be free to scour the land in search of mortals with pure souls. He will feast upon them to increase his strength, then he will have his vengeance on the surviving immortals who dared to deceive him.

Long ago, Tirasel, along with the other Gods, tricked Evoka into entering the Underworld. They trapped him there in the hope that he would never return, but the Land of the Dead is no longer his prison. Evoka is now free to do as he wishes, and the future of the world will be written in the blood of his enemies.

Having won the contest, you collect your winnings and leave the building. (Add ten **Crimson Coins** to your belongings.) You head onwards and eventually find yourself back at the town square.

If you have the word **Time** written on your Character Sheet, turn to **97**.

If not, turn to **15**.

The entrance creaks open, and you see a tall, scrawny man standing behind a dusty counter. He is dressed in dark clothes with a patch over his eyes. You gather that he is blind, but a crow sits silently upon his shoulder, watching you with gleaming black orbs.

Clutter fills the cobwebbed shelves, but amidst the chaos, several items catch your attention.

Items you might like to buy:

An **Enchanted, Emerald Bracelet**, said to bring
luck (One available) Cost: **six Crimson Coins**

Enchanted, Spiked Climbing Boots
(One pair available) Cost: **four Crimson Coins**

Magic Gloves
(One pair available) Cost: **five Crimson Coins**

Items you might like to sell:

If you possess a **Tarnished Gem**
the trader will offer you **two Crimson Coins** for it

If you have a **Small Goblin Statue**
the trader will offer you **three Crimson Coins** for it

If you have a **Small Fairy Statue**
he will buy it for **three Crimson Coins**

For a **Sapphire Ring**
he will give you **four Crimson Coins**

For **Ariana's Necklace**
he will give you **six Crimson Coins**

For a **Black Crystal Necklace**
he will give you **six Crimson Coins**

When you are done, turn to **361**.

The Amossans have suffered many casualties but, despite the odds, they appear to be winning the fight. Their confidence has remained strong and their skill in combat is outshining the enemy's. The undead horde starts to crumble under the onslaught and their numbers begin to dwindle. Soon, a cluster of just fifty Skeletons remain, crowded together in a tightly packed group. You smash your way into the heart of their ranks, leaving a wreckage of bones in your wake, and your comrades quickly follow you into the depths of the fray. As the final, fierce battle erupts, a one-armed Skeleton springs towards you, with its curved sword raised above its head.

If you leap foward and try to hack off its remaining arm, before it can strike, turn to **353**.

If you swipe at its head, hoping to smash its skull, turn to **399**.

If you hold your ground and adopt a defensive stance, turn to **378**.

Do you possess the special ability of **Haste**?

If you do, turn to **372**.

If not, turn to **355**.

You swallow a large mouthful, then your eyes suddenly begin to water. You feel light-headed, then your vision blurs, and you are forced to sit down and steady yourself on a stool by the bar.

Your throat has been burnt by the potent brew.

(Reduce your **Life Force** by one point.)

"What do you think?" asks the bartender.

"I think this stuff could kill a bear," you say, with an unimpressed expression.

"You are probably right," he nods. "It is a good drink. So, what brings you to our fine town?"

Turn to **87**.

The effects of the gas are only temporary, and your vision quickly returns to normal. You can now see the little creature up ahead, running as fast as he can. As you draw nearer, he suddenly runs up onto an arched bridge and leaps from the edge towards the water. You see that he has landed in a small dinghy that was tied beneath the crossing, and he is now rowing away, laughing with triumph. The walls of the houses come directly up to the river, so there is no bank. However, his boat is pushing through heaps of floating rubbish, so you could spring after him across the bobbing debris.

If you continue the chase, you would risk falling into the stinking water. If you are willing to take that chance, turn to **358**.

If you abandon the persuit, turn to **374**.

397

You suddenly hear the squeaking of many rats, and you feel the vermin swarming through the water. You grab their tails and hurl them into the shadows, but several clamber onto your back and try to bite you with their sharp teeth.

You knock them off and swish your blade through the water. Moments later, you realise that the sea level is rising swiftly, and the creaking from the vessel has become more pronounced. The rats hasten towards the hatchway, as if hoping to escape the ship.

Roll one dice to see if luck is with you.

If you roll a one or a two, turn to **170**.

If you roll a three or higher, turn to **369**.

398

You suffer no injury at all. You land safely on the walkway, then you glance back as the other bridge sinks beneath the steaming surface. Turn to **123**.

399

You slice through the Skeleton's neck, sending its head flying into the crowd. However, its wretched body continues forward, and it brings the pommel of its sword crashing down onto your shoulder.

(Lose one **Life Force**.)

If you are still alive, you cleave through your enemy, splitting it in two, then it crumples onto the floor and ceases to move. Turn to **363**.

400

Luck is with you! The lightning not only collides with your magical blade, but it is also reflected back at your enemy!

Evoka is hit by the full force of his own attack, then his terrible scream shakes the chamber. He staggers backwards, writhing around whilst clutching his face in agony. As you watch, he accidentally stumbles through the portal and instantly vanishes. He has been transported back into the Land of the Dead, but your enemy does not immediately realise what has happened, for he has been overwhelmed by the blinding anguish of his own curse!

Grasping this opportunity, you leap up and rush forward. With the Dream-Sword gripped tightly in both hands, you swipe at the edge of the magical doorway.

As the blade connects with the fissure, there is a sudden flash of light, then an explosive boom throws you backwards off of your feet. You tumble to a halt, striking your head against the rocky island as a rush of wind sweeps over you.

Then silence.

You are unconscious for several minutes before your senses return. When you open your eyes, you find yourself lying close to the edge of the bubbling lava. The Dream-Sword has vanished, but so has the dreaded portal! Evoka has been trapped on the far side, back in the Land of the Dead!

Against all the odds, you have defeated your enemy! You have destroyed the only gateway between his world and yours, and you have saved all the people of the land. You want to leap up and cry out with victory, but the strain of your ordeal suddenly sweeps upon you. The Dream-Sword was numbing your pain and boosting your speed, but its effects have vanished. The **Enchanted Bracelet / Glittering Bone Charm**, which helped to save you from Evoka's final spell, has also disappeared; its magic has been depleted and it has crumbled into dust. (Remove the artefact and the **Dream-Sword** from your inventory.) A great exhaustion consumes you, so you collapse onto your side and tumble into a dreamless void.

You may now turn to the next page
and read the *Epilogue*.

Epilogue

When you wake, you are no longer in the cave. You are back in the King's palace, curled up in bed, and by the look of your healed wounds you have been here for several weeks. Pelanthius is sitting on a nearby chair, and he is clearly pleased that you have awoken.

In the weeks that follow, you enjoy a host of festivities that are held in your honour. King Faranen puts on a series of banquets, and your belly is stuffed with good food and fine wine. Countless times over, you are asked to tell the story of your clash with Evoka, and the people of the palace listen with bated breaths.

On a cold, late evening, while you are sitting on the balcony of your room, your adventurous spirit begins to gnaw at you, so you decide to travel home before the sea freezes and the bay becomes clogged with ice.

Before you leave, Faranen gives you a new suit of **Hardy Leather Armour** and a mighty sword named **Elandril**, which has been in his family for generations. You thank him, but the king shakes his head. "It is I who am thankful," he says. "You saved my Kingdom and all the people of Amossa. I hope my gifts serve you well."

You nod and say goodbye.

For the next few weeks you travel south with the Wizard, back across the rolling sea and down the coast. You enjoy many adventures along the way, and you eventually part company at the town of RedBrook. If you have any **Health Potions**, you drink the last of them on the long trek home. On a cold evening, you find yourself back in your castle by the lake.

Winter has now tightened its grip, and fierce snow storms batter the region. You keep the fireplace burning with logs from the forest, and for the next few months you remain tucked away in the safety of your home. When the early signs of spring finally arrive, there comes a brisk tapping at your window. It is night, and rain is pattering in the darkness, so you are surprised at the prospect of a visitor. A gust of wind blows in when you open the door, then you see a little hunched figure with a dripping hat standing on the step. It is the Witch, who you met at the start of your adventure.

"Greetings," she says with a shiver, in her familiar, croaky voice. Without waiting for an invite, she shuffles past you and climbs into your chair by the fireplace.

"Ah yes," she intones, "much warmer in here. Very pleasant. But where is your cauldron? And look at that hideously clean ceiling! You really need to sort this place out. A home is not a home until a few cobwebs have gathered around the beams."

"I do not need decorating tips from a Witch," you assure her. "Now why are you here, or did you just come to offend me?"

"I have some bad news," she says. "It regards the three Demons who unleashed Evoka."

Your eyes narrow. "What of them?" you ask.

"I slew two of them with the help of my sisters, but the third Demon, Golgorast, escaped. He proved much more cunning and dangerous than we expected, so I have decided to let you deal with him instead."

"You have broken your word," you tell her. "You said you would deal with the three Demons, if I dealt with Evoka. My part of the bargain has been fulfilled."

The Witch shrugs. "I am not very good at keeping promises," she admits. "But I did deal with two out of the three. Anyhow, I came a long way to speak to you, so the least you could do is offer me a drink. You must have a bottle of eyeball wine, hidden nearby."

You offer her a mug of water instead, but she merely stares at it in disgust. "You can tip that out of the window," she mutters. "I guess you are saving the good stuff for yourself." She pulls a bottle of bubbling slime from her pocket and starts to sip on that instead.

You sit down opposite the Witch, then she continues

to talk. "I came here to give you a warning," she says. "Golgorast is determined to kill you, even more so after his last failed attempt. With his two brethren dead, he no longer has the power to open another Demon Gate, but that does not mean that you are safe. He is the last of Zanack's bloodline. He will not return to Cair Nurath in disgrace, not until he bears news of your death, so it is only a matter of time until he starts to cause you trouble once more."

"Have you any idea of his next move?" you ask.

"The future is hard to predict," she answers, "but if my crystal ball is correct, he will head west to Miner's Island. He will build a new, dark lair in the heart of a bleak mountain, then he will reveal his next scheme." She watches you with a beady eye, which you can just make out beneath the tangled nest of her hair. "If I were you, I would go and hunt him down. If you don't, it will mean more grief for you in the long run."

She passes you a map and jabs her finger towards a section of the parchment, showing you where to go.

"I have just returned from the east coast," you say. "If you are correct, I will have to travel all the way to Kostaria's *west* coast. On foot, I would not reach those shores until midsummer. I should probably tell Pelanthius of this, he may be able to-"

"Forget the Wizards," she interrupts. "They are trying to cure an outbreak of plague in the south. If you want to deal with Golgorast, you will have to do it alone. If you are wise, you will set off soon." She climbs out of the chair and shuffles back towards the front door. "Now, I must be off," she says. "The Witches are having a get-together at midnight tomorrow, and I cannot be late for it." She pushes open your door, allowing the cold rain to sweep in. "Goodbye, foul human. I doubt I will see you again, but doing business with you has been an interesting experience."

"What is your name?" you ask.

She looks back with a wink. "That would be telling," she says. "I have good reason to keep my name secret, but that is another story. You can just call me the Nameless Witch." With that, she hops onto her broomstick and soars upwards, vanishing into the pitch-dark night with a loud cackle.

You stand by the door with a stern expression. You know that you will not be able to sleep soundly until Golgorast is brought to justice.

You decide to get what rest you can, so you clamber into bed and bury yourself beneath the covers. The clouds gradually pass, the land grows quiet, and a cold moon casts its light over the lake.

Early next morning, you grab the **Witch's Map** and decide to set off in search of your enemy. You want to travel fast and light, so you pack only the items that you deem necessary. You don your **Hardy Leather Armour**, pick up **Elandril**, and fill your money pouch with **twenty Crimson Coins**. You lock everything else in your vault before heading to the front door.

The rain has died and a quiet world, dotted with the buds of spring, stretches out before you. You set off into the wild landscape with your hand resting on the hilt of your sword.

It is high time that Golgorast paid for his crimes, and you are not going to sit around and give him time to plan his next attack. The road ahead may well be dangerous, but a faint smile is etched across your face.

What fun would a quiet summer be for you, anyway?

This page is a 'save point.' The special abilities which you chose at the start of this quest are yours to keep forever; you will never lose them, and you should mark them with a 'P' (for permanent) on your Character Sheet. With each new adventure, you will choose more special abilities to add to the ones you already have.

Your adventure continues in book three, entitled:

The Curse of Golgorast

About the Author/Illustrator

Dave Lewis spent much of his young life
living on a small sailing boat.
Out on the waves, the rough seas and changing
environments fuelled his imagination.
There was no modern technology on board,
so reading, drawing and writing
were his primary entertainment.
After studying animation at university,
he worked as both a musician
and a freelance artist.
At length, he began to illustrate
and publish his own books.
In addition to his creative projects, Dave also
worked part-time in college art departments,
supporting children with special needs.
He lives in a village in England,
near the outskirts of London.

Printed in Great Britain
by Amazon